Edward J. Miller

Froggy Bottom

FROGGY BOTTOM

A One-Room School in Indiana

1922

Tale of a Young Teacher

Nancy Todd

Copyright © 1995 by Nancy Todd
All Rights Reserved

Library of Congress
Catalog Card Number
95-090891

GET Printing, Inc.
Goshen, Indiana

First Printing, October 1995
Printed on Recycled Paper

Printed in the United States of America

*To my mother—and all others like her
who have dedicated and devoted their lives
to teaching the youth of our country.*

Miss Helen Todd
(the future Mrs. Helen Christner)
Froggy Bottom School, 1922

FOREWARD

Reasons for writing books are many and varied. *Froggy Bottom* was written for two principal ones: to pay tribute to my mother, Mrs. Helen Christner, who has devoted her entire adult life, more than forty years to teaching the young of our country and secondly to attempt, in some small way, to preserve the heritage of the now extinct institution, the one-room school.

Froggy Bottom is a fictionalized tale depicting the life and happenings of a young, inexperienced school teacher's first year in a one-room school. Set deep in northern Indiana's socially and religiously conservative agricultural heartland, the story begins in September and takes the reader through to the end of April, the length of a rural school year in 1922. Although all characters and even the setting of *Froggy Bottom* are imaginary, the book is, in truth, patterned after the life of my mother.

Related through the words and thoughts of an unseasoned and immature schoolmarm, *Froggy Bottom* portrays more than the events of a country school in the early twenties. It also reveals a basic philosophy which permeated the "little red schoolhouse." Here was found an atmosphere of discipline, responsibility, cooperation–sharing, giving, loving–which formed the moral and intellectual building blocks to create the character and strengths of our rural youngsters. From these four walls–structured in Bible readings, poetry, classical literature and patriotism and flanked with the sayings of the "Little Red Hen" and the "The Little Engine that Could"–emanated the source and direction which would determine the kind of man or woman the pupil would become in the future. Even in our so-called progressive world of today, if possible, we would still seek to emulate the formation which produced that distinguished group of individuals who claim the one-room school as their alma mater.

In preparing this book I asked my mother what she found to be the outstanding contribution of the one-room school. She thought for some time. Finally she said, "instilling a sense of duty–no one ever refused or did not complete a required task no matter how disagreeable or disliked it might be." Always the school teacher she then added, "We often quoted the words inscribed on Robert E. Lee's bust... 'Do your duty in all things. You cannot do more. You should never wish to do less.' "

Many were the teachers such as my mother who spent their teaching years in the one-room school. They were often unheralded in the outside world but they were never forgotten in the hearts of their pupils. This cadre of educators who worked with so little to create so much deserve our most rewarding salute. The days of the one-room school, their teachers and pupils, are now gone forever, however, let them not by forgotten–they rendered far too much for such an unworthy demise.

Small as it is, *Froggy Bottom* owes its creation to a myriad of individuals, too numerous to thank individually. It is the author's hope that her gratitude is adequately expressed through the book's ensuing pages; within them are to be found many a suggestive thread which has been woven into the over-all tale.

There is, however, one individual, in particular, who must be publicly acknowledged; she is my sister, Phyllis Begley. Without her unstinting support and encouragement, *Froggy Bottom* would never have been created. For years she has actively and steadfastly championed the cause to protect and preserve the treasured heritage of "The Little Red Schoolhouse"; one outgrowth of her interest has been this little book.

Another individual to whom I wish to express my gratitude is to the young, talented illustrator, Beth McKechnie, whose sketches have so poignantly captured the revealing spirit of the one-room school.

May the readers of *Froggy Bottom* find within a few kernels of beauty, humor and pocketsful of remembrances.

The Author

Marbella, Spain
September 1995

SEPTEMBER

It is the first Monday after Labor Day–that's when all the Indiana schools begin their fall session and this is my first day of school–as a teacher. Two weeks ago I had no idea I would be teaching this year. What am I saying? It was only last weekend that the Superintendent of Schools contacted my father to see if I were available–he never even consulted me which I suppose is natural enough as he had insisted upon (much to my own objection) and paid for my twelve-week course which turned me into a qualified teacher of the first eight grades in the elementary system! Both of us had given up that there would be any return on his investment this year.

Froggy Bottom (that's the name of my school) is located deep in farm country, six miles east of Waterford and eight miles west of Wakarusa. During the week I am to be taking room and board at the Eli Bontrager home. Fortunately they live only a little more than half-a-mile from the school. All around this is a most convenient arrangement. I sleep in their daughter Agnes' room; she works in Goshen as a hired girl. On late Friday afternoon Mrs. B. will take me into town by horse and buggy when she will pick up Agnes, and then she will do the reverse on Sunday afternoon.

I gather Mrs. B. is rather lonely which is most understandable as her husband rarely says a word. They have only one child at home anymore, so I suppose I will be sort of a daughter substitute, which suits me fine for life here is so much different than any I have ever known. Mrs. B. loves to chat and is a born-informer. With her innate capacities she soon will have ironed out the social wrinkles for me. It is understood having a teacher as a boarder elevates one's standing in the community, so Mrs. B. will be bound to see that I become a shining example in the field of pedagogy.

After a full day I am sitting at Mrs. B.'s dining room table trying to recapture the impressions of this opening chapter in my life as a teacher in an Indiana one-room schoolhouse.

The day began early. By six o'clock, I had dressed and was downstairs only to find everyone else in the household well into their day's activities. The only evidence that Mr. B. had been there were the crumbs around his egg-stained breakfast plate. The kitchen was heavily scented with fresh baking odors. Mrs. B. bustled around saying I must eat. I could only manage a cup of coffee and the gooey cinnamon bun hot from the oven which I knew she had made especially for me. I was nervous.

Without words Mrs. B. simply took over. Bessie, the mare, was patiently waiting outside. My books and papers were bundled into the buggy. Still in silence we wobbled off. Soon the Froggy Bottom School came into sight and it could have been the prototype for America's "Little Red Schoolhouse." Situated in the back center of a treeless one-half acre plot, the worn bricks, the belfry, the four south windows, looking like huge sad eyes, the flight of pyramid-shaped cement steps leading to the wooden double door, all seemed to say, "Open me up and make me happy."

Mrs. B. led me through the central foyer. There were cloakrooms on either side.

"The one to the west side is for the boys, big and little, and to the east for all the girls. They hang their coats on the hooks and in the winter leave their boots there. Their lunch pails are put on the window sills."

A type of wainscoting, dark narrow wooden paneling, lines the lower four feet of these halls and the interior schoolroom. The ceiling is very high.

A strong and heavy odor, a mixture of stale chalk dust and the creosote used to clean and stain the wooden floor, permeates the room. Mrs. B., I learned, was not just being motherly, it was her official duty to show me the school as she was in charge of its cleaning and general upkeep.

Six windows light the main schoolroom. Two on either side of the cloakrooms on the south side, two to the east and two to the west; all with deep sills and reaching from about two feet from the ceiling to the wainscoting. A wide wooden border frames each window and each is decorated at each corner and midway up by an unusually beautiful square plaque featuring a carved bunch of grapes set in their leaves and tendrils.

Mrs. B. pointed these out saying, "I've often wondered who made them–I'd like a set for my house."

A wooden framed, octagonal-shaped Seth Thomas clock hangs in the center of the windows to the east.

Mrs. B. led me up to the teacher's desk. All its drawers were slightly pulled out.

"So there won't be any mice."

We placed the books and papers we carried in our arms on top. The space on which the desk stands juts out from a raised platform which extends all the way to the west wall and to the corner of the cupboard on the east. The wall behind and above the platform is sectioned slate blackboard. Directly opposite my desk, in front of the entrance coming in from the foyer, stands a gigantic, circular, asbestos-lined stove.

"The big boys will help carry in the wood–it's in the shed. In the winter they stack a whole day's supply right there in the entrance–it's a good heater, this stove."

The rows of desks begin with the small sizes on the east side in line with the end of the platform. Each grade is a size larger with five or six seats to a row.

"This year there won't be need of any more desks–but, you can see, we can add if necessary."

The seats and desks of the first three grades are attached by their iron feet to parallel wooden three inch wide sturdy slats making these rows portable. The other desks and seats are screwed into the floor.

Mrs. B. then pointed to a low wooden bench in front of the 5th, 6th and 7th grade rows. Its high back and long seat are highly polished by years of use.

"That's the recitation bench."

What a plain and stark room it is! In the five-shelved, open-faced cupboard Mrs. B. showed me where the American flag was kept; it was carefully folded and tucked into the lower corner.

"This is the library. We have a few fine books. *Pilgrim's Progress* was a gift from Mrs. Martin. The Bible from Mrs. S. K. Yoder. An 'English' donated all these magazines."

Proudly she pointed to a shelf which was filled with tattered *National Geographics.*

"The school board gave this set of World Books and the dictionary."

Both were well-used and would have been rejected by any secondhand book dealer. The Webster's Dictionary was huge and particularly dilapidated.

The area in front of the cupboard is vacant–a long rectangle of open space.

"Here in the winter, the children play games. Often the teacher allows them to use chalk and draw in squares to play hopscotch," Mrs. B. explained.

It was time to ring the first bell at eight o'clock. "Now, I must leave you. God bless you, child. Have a good day." She smiled almost coyly. "I'll say a little prayer for you."

This bell is the signal for most pupils to leave their homes to arrive before the second and last bell at 8:30 a.m. Next the flag had to be hoisted on the pole at the foot of the steps. Then I wanted to inspect the grounds and the outside buildings.

The unpainted shed on the west side has no door in its jamb; inside it is filled already with neatly stacked cords of wood. Directly behind it at the far northwest corner of the school stands the boys' two-holer toilet. It also is devoid of paint and many a boy's pocketknife has pierced its wooden sides to make a peephole. Inside hooked on a heavy wire was a flapping Sears Roebuck catalog. My education was beginning. The girls' toilet on the northeast corner is similar in every respect except there are no peep holes and a shoulder high wooden fence guards its entrance, probably because it is located near the road.

The pump is at the edge of the playground on the southwest corner near the ditch. It is rusty, erect like a sentinel, but surprisingly it gushed icy cold water after two hefty pushes on the handle. There is no playground equipment. The ground surrounding the school is hard, caked turf with little-to-no grass. I did find a scarred softball and bat in the front foyer. Certainly there is ample space for a baseball diamond.

By 8:30 a.m. the schoolroom had filled up. The children, wide-eyed but strangely silent, took seats as if they had been told where to sit. No parents came to greet me on this day. The new first graders were placed in seats by older pupils.

Awkward is hardly the word. I truly do not know how I began. Something like, "I am your new teacher–Miss Todd is my name. I am glad to be here and I am looking forward to teaching you this year."

No response at all. So then I suggested that to begin the day, all should stand, put their hands to their hearts and repeat an "Allegiance to the Flag." This proved to be mostly a monologue as I had very few and then only mumbling participants. I attributed this to shyness.

Next I took a roster of the names of the students and their grades which I record here for posterity!

ROSTER

First Grade: (3) . . . . Norman Knox
Amos Miller
Katie Yoder

Second Grade: (4) . . . . Emma Stutzman
John Henry Bender
Sadie Smucker
Susie Cripe

Third Grade: (3) . . . . Anna Mae Weaver
Norma Jean Herr
Clara Sue Good

Fourth Grade: (2) . . . . Orval Miller
                                     Alma Yoder

Fifth Grade: (3) . . . . Vilma Knox
                                Aaron Michael
                                Omar Hostetler

Sixth Grade: (4) . . . . Robert Hartman
                          James Buchanan Martin
                                Gladys Rohrer
                                Charles Weaver

Seventh Grade: (4) . . . . Grace Hunsberger
                                Abner Hostetler
                                Christian Yoder
                                Mary Michael

Eighth Grade: (2) . . . . Dorothy Mast
                                Daniel Troyer

There are twenty-five pupils in my schoolroom. The smallest number being two in a class and the largest number being four.

Mrs. B. just came in and looked over the names.

"Here in the country we are all plain people but some are plainer than others. I see I've a lot of teachin' to do for you'll never understand some of their ways if I don't."

She patted me on the shoulder. "Time to go to bed– 6:30 comes right soon–you can finish your writin' up another day."

True, I am too tired to continue.

<u>Wednesday evening</u>: Again I am writing at Mrs. B.'s dining room table. I am still exhausted but if I don't write up my experiences as they happen–and there are so many new ones–I won't remember them.

Going back to my first day–Monday definitely did not end up on the positive side of the ledger. There was no doubt that I was the object of great curiosity much of which was explained to me by the very forthright Mrs. B.

"Child, what can you expect? These young'uns never before had a woman teacher–and then to have a 'foreigner' like you with uncovered, bobbed hair wearing that sinfully short skirt almost showing your knees. Here it is usual for females to have their skirts within eight inches of the floor. And your shoes! Those new-fangled ones with a buttoned strap across the instep and those two-inch heels. It weren't in my place to say nothing but now that you asked."

Believe me when Mrs. B. tackles a subject she launches a withering barrage that does not lessen until finished.

"None of these children has ever seen, at least right at hand, a woman's legs covered with silk stockings. They never saw the likes of you. Then you added that long strand of pearl beads around your neck. Can you imagine what they went home and told their parents? No, you certainly can not!"

The next day, Tuesday, I arrived early. I had already finished my routine chores and was seated at my desk trying to organize names and faces when in walked my eighth-grade girl.

Without ceremony she began, "You probably don't know my name. I'm Dorothy Mast, a repeater as is Daniel. Our kind don't go to high school. Next year I will go live with relatives in Ohio for a time."

This was a point of which I was aware. The Amish do not believe in higher education. They feel that more secular education exposes their children to the evils and temptations of the outside world. In order to circumvent Indiana's compulsory education law–all children are to study until sixteen years of age–they, the Amish, frequently begin the child's schooling at seven years of age, have them repeat the eighth grade and if still under the age limit, their families send them to relatives in Ohio, Pennsylvania or some other state where they have Amish settlements. To date our officials have wisely closed their eyes to these actions.

Suddenly the big girl became shy, "If you want I can help you–I know all the lessons–I can explain how we do certain things so you won't make so many mistakes."

For the first time I looked carefully at this tall, dark-haired near-woman. Her hair was parted in the middle, smoothly pulled down and covered by a white organdy cap with two hanging ties. She wore a long, solid dark green one-piece dress with a high round neck and long sleeves. Over this she wore a sleeveless organdy smock-like garment which I had been told was called an apron. To my utter amazement she was barefoot. My startled look must have given her needed courage.

Laughingly she said, "We are very savin' people–besides it's still too hot for shoes."

She was right. Temperatures had soared to the low nineties. This year was unseasonably hot for September. I could only smile weakly.

She continued seriously, "I'm being raised by my grandmother. You see my mother ran off and married an 'English' who turned out to be 'no good' according to Grandma. My mother has been excommunicated–it's like being dead for my people. None of us have ever seen nor heard from her since she left. Daily I am a reminder of her sins–she broke my Grandma's heart. Grandpa has never spoken her name since she took off."

The wall clock chimed eight and I had to run to ring the first bell. Coming back I plied my self-appointed assistant with questions. It was readily agreed that my schedule of four major periods with a recess in between each and one hour for lunch was a good program.

Dorothy informed me that it was customary to read to the children. This is considered a treat and usually takes place after lunch on Friday afternoons. I should not, however, read them fairy tales or stories where animals talk and act like people because the Bishops frown upon such unnatural actions. And definitely there should not be stories with wizardry or magic!

This was all that we were able to cover before the youngsters began to arrive. This morning I had a big smile of greeting on my face. Dorothy's offered friendship had made a big difference in my mental outlook. I clearly felt more equipped to meet my charges.

This happy start had a quick squelch. To learn the pupil's names I decided to have them stand up and tell something about themselves, their family, where they lived, this type of introduction. This was a woeful experiment without any but mute results, that is, until I called the name "Orval Miller."

A sallow-faced, oval-headed fourth grader with scraggly blond locks hanging over his forehead stood erect and blurted out, "How old are you?"

Flabbergasted, I also blurted out, "Nineteen."

"Jist like Ma says, 'She ain't hardly dry behind the ears yet.'" His comment evidently was directed to his younger brother, Amos, in the first grade.

Blushing until my hair roots tingled, I decided we had enough social exchange for one morning. Lessons began with reading. Maybe edges are being smoothed but progress is quite agonizing. Yesterday, I was as glad for the ten o'clock recess as were the children.

This morning Mrs. Levi Bender brought her son, John Henry, to school. He is the only boy among four in the second grade. He hardly talks and the poor lad is cross-eyed. Jolly, portly and rosy-cheeked Mrs. Bender certainly paid this first visit to find out what kind of 'foreigner' was teaching here at Froggy Bottom. Neat in a black bonnet, she wore an ankle-length light gray cotton print dress covered with wee white flowers. Even with my meager education I knew she was not Amish which was later confirmed by Dorothy who told me she was Old Order German Baptist. Mrs. Bender, although curious, did come with a point to make as she stressed, "John Henry may be slow but he is thorough."

Whether I come up to Mrs. Bender's standards is yet to be known, but following her visit my news harbinger told me the plain people, particularly the Amish, do not believe that mentally retarded children should be segregated nor institutionalized. They are all God's creatures and all of them need each other, some more than others. The family from young to old, from weak to strong, work and live together as a unit. However, John Henry, although perhaps not the brightest of my pupils, is far from being retarded.

This brings me to my next point where I was again saved by Dorothy. There are three first graders—I had hit an impregnable wall. I simply could not make them understand me. Katie Yoder and Amos Miller knew nothing but "Pennsylvania Dutch."

As Dorothy so sagely put it, "We never had this problem before–all our other teachers spoke "Dutch."

"Dutch" is not the language from the Netherlands but a low German dialect. Still, I do not know it. School Board or not, I officially made Dorothy my assistant. What a load off my shoulders!

Little Katie and tubby Amos are both Amish. They are dressed exactly like adults only in miniature–she in her white-stringed head covering, bonnet and over-apron and he in his barn-door pants, suspenders and broad-brimmed hat.

Katie always looked down when I drew near and I thought this was because she was overly shy. Not true Dorothy told me; the real reason was one of fascination. She was attracted by my shoes, now very low oxfords, and in particular my silk hose. I asked Dorothy to ask her if she would like to touch them. Katie's blue eyes sparkled as her tiny hand reached out, hesitated and then gingerly felt my leg. She giggled and said something which Dorothy translated as "Store bought?"

As for the third member of the first grade, Dorothy classified Norman as being low "English." Norman is a very small boy for six years with enormous black eyes and deep eye shadows and a shock of matted auburn hair. He always appears to be half asleep. He looks, smells, and acts as if he sleeps and lives permanently in his faded and patched overalls. Water and soap are apparently unknown quantities in the Knox household.

His sister, Vilma, is a fifth grader and old beyond her years. She has but one tattered cotton dress, no shoes, only old house slippers. She, however, does try to comb her long blonde hair and wash her face.

"A sad story," is how Dorothy began. "Nobody here is ever on relief but the Knoxs are—we don't believe in acceptin' any kind of help from the government. They live on the other side of the swamp in an old shack. Their father ran away with another woman and the mother is sickly. She dug up a plot to raise beans and potatoes which she tries to sell but she is so poorly that she spends most of her time in bed. The children pick wild berries in season—raspberries, blackberries, elderberries—and go peddlin' from house to house. Our womenfolk try to help but some of our men aren't so kind. They say Mrs. Knox is in bed with her bottle of schnapps."

Mrs. B. just turned down the Aladdin lamp, so I must end for the day. It is off to bed.

<u>Friday</u>: A glorious day! I have taught school for one week and it seems like forever. As I walked to school everything seemed so fresh and bright; the temperatures have fallen and there is just a tinge of autumn in the breeze. Could it be that the foliage around the pond has begun to change or is it my imagination?

This pond, Froggy Bottom—which strangely enough I have not mentioned—evidently was so named because of its amphibian inhabitants. It lies across the road from the school. It is a natural winter playground for children, both skaters and sledders, for its north side is fully backed by a high but treeless hill with the pond at its base.

How happy I am to be leaving with Mrs. B. this afternoon for a weekend with my family. Before dismissing the children at 3:30 p.m. I told them per my counselor, Dorothy, they must all recite a Bible verse, which they will learn during the weekend, for Monday morning's opening session.

— ♦ —

I don't think I stopped talking all weekend. There was a crowd at home. How could it be otherwise with a grown family of nine? True, my oldest sister, Mae, has married and my oldest brother "Buzz" is working away from home. Still with Mother and Dad and the rest of the brood plus a few of our collected friends, it is always a house full.

Jennie, the beauty of the family and my confidant, has always been most conscious of clothes and appearance. She was delighted to hear that I was considered quite a fashion model in my teaching position. She did not quite understand the significance of my story–perhaps it would be better if I were to say I did not make my students' reaction to my appearance at all clear. For I, too, rightly or wrongly, also enjoyed portraying myself in the light of a certain adulation. Many times in the past, the Todd family when financially poor found itself on the bottom rung of the social ladder and simply because we did not have the proper clothes to wear.

This weekend Jennie was particularly light-hearted and generous. She had made an appointment at the beauty parlor for me to have my hair marcelled. It was her treat–so how could I refuse. Even as it was being done, I had a fearful premonition as to the reaction of "my" plain people.

Jennie chortled, "What a sensation! Your children are going to be so proud of their beautiful schoolmarm."

Jennie had also made a blind date for me. She and her favorite beau and Glen, a student from Goshen College (a Mennonite school), and I went roller-skating at Blosser's Park on an island in the Elkhart River, where the nickelodeon plays all the popular songs of the day. Glen is an excellent skater. He actually taught me to dance to "Everybody's Doin' It" and "Alexander's Ragtime Band." It was wonderful fun but I am certain the College does not know there is dancing on skates. They definitely would not approve.

Sunday afternoon came and I should have known that Mrs. B. would be far from subtle. As I climbed into the buggy she quipped, "Whatever happened to your head?"

I answered meekly, "I went to the beauty parlor."

Incredulously she again asked, "You paid to look like that?"

Still my spirits could not be dampened and I rode them high into Monday morning when a pop-eyed pupil population rotely recited their Bible verses. As I called Orval Miller's name I thought, "This will be it." And it was.

After his verse Orval questioned, "Did you get caught up in an egg beater?"

No answer this time, but when I came to Grace Hunsberger, she sweetly asked, "Are you wearing a wig, Miss Todd?" to which I shook my head slowly.

Just before the first recess I told the children that in each of the toilets there were now rolls of toilet tissue which were to be used sparingly as they were expensive. Actually I bought this lot from my own savings but I hoped to be reimbursed by the trustee at the end of the month. Just as I finished I heard Omar stage-whisper to his fellow fifth grader, Aaron, "It'll be better than corn cobs."

At lunch time to establish a policy of "Clean Hands Before Eating," I named Bobby Hartman as <u>Chief Custodian of the Water Pump</u> for the week. Bobby is taking his appointment very seriously and has enlisted the aid of his two sixth grade cohorts, Charlie and James B. Everyone was soon in line, doused and splashed clean. These three are <u>individually</u> bright and full of the old Nick; <u>together</u> they are smoldering dynamite. What one doesn't think of, the other two will. The "Clean Hands" system will have to be modified when colder weather arrives.

Everyone brings their lunches and we all sit down at our desks to eat. Mrs. B. prepares mine in a brown paper sack, usually two sandwiches of sliced chicken or other meat, a piece of fruit, an apple or pear, and a piece of cake or cookies. Most of the children carry little round covered tins with a handle. James B. Martin has a shiny new box type. Most of the children eat much the same as I do, sandwiches with fruit and a sweet of sorts.

As I sat down I could not help but watch Daniel Troyer (he is my other eighth grade repeater) out of the corner of my eye. Daniel is a loner, very respectful but always aloof and withdrawn. Wide-shouldered, sturdy with a soft dark down covering his upper lip, he can only be described as gentle. He rarely speaks but when he does, his voice already belongs to the lower register. Carefully he removed his wire-rimmed glasses, folded them and just as carefully put them into their eye case, placing it in the middle of the pencil slot on his desk. He methodically placed his lunch on the desk top, but before touching it, he closed his eyes and bent his head.

Dorothy, never missing much, told me after lunch without my asking, it was a custom among the Amish to offer a silent prayer before and after meals. She also explained that all day long, Daniel sat studying the Bible in German. Although the language spoken is "Pennsylvania Dutch," the religious services are held in German, and everyone is expected to study this language.

—◆—

Although it certainly was not expected of Froggy Bottom's schoolteacher, I nightly helped Mrs. B. peel pears for canning.

"This old Bartlett tree must be over fifty years old—every fall, no matter what the winds or lightening has done to it, we have pears a-plenty. Eli says it will probably out last us all."

These evenings were a source of real joy—and an added learning experience. Conversation never stopped until the last pear was halved and peeled.

"When I was a girl Mother would put up as many as five hundred quarts a season—vegetables, all kinds of beans, but mostly fruits—cherries, peaches and pears were the main stays."

I was soon to discover that in the country people have little time to read—and even if there is an opportunity many do it with difficulty. Of course, there is no electricity out here and even if there were, religion would not permit it in many homes and there can be no radios. Rare is it when a group, be it women, men or mixed, does not soon begin a discussion sounding something like "Eldon Martin who is a first cousin once removed of Eli Smoker, married Jonathan Weaver's daughter whose mother was the half-sister to Aaron Graybill's wife who was a Pletcher." These genealogical sessions can go on for hours, rounding out points on family trees. As I am a "foreigner," Mrs. B. has to give up this conversational passion. This lack certainly does not deter the formidable Mrs. B.

"Our meals are heavy and rich—so you'll always find sweet and sour relishes or pickles on the table. Eli particularly likes my watermelon rind preserve and chow-chow."*

* Basically a pickle relish with onions, cauliflower and green tomatoes added to enhance the condiment.

"Mrs. Bontrager, do you think I could tell the children an Aesop's fable—the one about the ant and the grasshopper? Do you know it?"

Mrs. B. just cocked her head to the left, so I went on explaining, "It is about a little ant who works hard saving up food while the grasshopper lolls around in the summer doing nothing; then comes the winter and he has to beg the ant for food. There is a moral to the story: it is thrifty to prepare for the wants of tomorrow. I find great similarity to the lives of farm people."

"Now, why could you not be telling this charming tale? Besides I believe you will find your Mr. Aesop took the idea for his story from the Bible itself."

"Dorothy told me the Bishops frown on such stories where animals or insects talk."

"Maybe that is true for the Old Order Amish—but the Bishops are not nearly as inflexible as Dorothy believes. They know elementary schools are for youngsters of all religions. They view these years in the public school system as an opportunity for their young people to see the ways of others."

Here Mrs. B. gave forth a robust chuckle, "And to 'reject their sinful influences selectively' as their Bishop Yoder once said to me.

"Remember child, you only have six pupils who belong to the Amish denomination—that's only one-fourth of your student body."

Mrs. B. looked at me very quizzically, "You still don't know the basic differences among us plain people, do you?"

My negative head shake brought out the dominant lecturer in Mrs. B.

"I have no intention of going back to the 16th century when Jacob Ammann and Menno Simons began to have their religious disagreements in Europe. I only want to describe briefly and perhaps point out the basic differences in the overall picture. Here in our community we have two major and distinctive religious bodies, the Amish and the Mennonites. The Old Orders are, of course, the most conservative in either of these denominations. Eli and I belong to the Reform Mennonites—over the years our group has evolved becoming more progressive in our attitudes."

All Mrs. B. needed was a lectern to stand behind. She could be Froggy Bottom's advocate of-and-for religious rights.

"Amish people look within—they are not interested in changing the world—they only wish to protect their environment, their homes and way of living, their beliefs. They wish to be separated from the outside world and for this reason they do not want their children to receive a higher education. The farm and farming is the center of their immediate world."

Evidently I sighed deeply for she stopped and looked at me. "I know it is very complicated and today I will not make this entire presentation clear, but in time you will come to know and to understand all of us much better."

Mrs. B. pushed away her kettle and got up, "I'll fix us a nice cup of tansy tea—it'll give us a little lift before I go on."

After a few sips she began again, "It is such a big subject and I want to discuss several more points before we go to bed.

"Contrary to the Amish way of thinking, the Mennonites believe in meeting and trying to help save the outside world. They have and are moving along with modern technology. They will allow electricity in their homes if it is available, central heating in their homes and telephones, but not the Amish. Many Mennonites have started to use tractors in farming–not the Old Order Mennonites nor Amish for they both still use horses for farming and transportation. The Mennonites believe in higher education so that many of our people have left the farms and entered into certain professions such as those arts and sciences which offer to serve mankind–missionary work, teaching and medical fields.

"Here in Indiana, the Amish have various branches, Old Order and Beachy. And we Mennonites have quite a few– Old Order, Conservative, Reform, Holdeman and Burkholder. We also have other plain people–Old Order German Baptists, Old Order Lutherans, Dunkard Brethren.

"Many differences in the break-off branches have been caused by conflicts over dress and appearance and use of modern-day conveniences. For example, the Beachy Amish broke away because many of their members wanted to use field tractors and attend services in meeting houses rather than in the homes."

"How does an outsider, like myself, tell by looking what group the man or woman belongs to?"

"That's not easy to answer simply. An Amish man, if married, wears a beard but no mustache. They used to be called "hook and eyers" for on their Sunday frock coats they have no buttons. The modern day Mennonite man is clean-shaven and wears buttoned coats.

"Dear me, I am getting myself into hot water. All women of our plain people wear head coverings. In the Bible it is written a woman's head must always be covered in the sight of God. These coverings differ in design, each order has their own distinctive model and manner in which it is worn.

"Child, that is enough. The pears are finished." Mrs. B. had actually run down—no wonder, it was nearly midnight.

— ♦ —

My second weekend at home was very busy. Jennie and Mother had gone to visit my Aunt Mattie who had been taken ill and I was left at home to take care of my two youngest sisters and prepare the meals for the family. Besides washing and ironing my clothes, I wanted to make curtains for my schoolroom. I had stopped at Kline's in Goshen to buy material and curtain rods. Formerly I had worked for Mr. K. and he generously gave me a marked reduction on some fine, white cheesecloth. I inveigled my nine-year old sister Irene into helping me sew the curtains and somehow we finished six pairs of Dutch-styled (half) curtains before Mrs. B. picked me up on Sunday afternoon.

Early Monday morning, armed with hammer and tacks, I successfully put up all the schoolroom curtains before 8:30 a.m. I viewed them with womanly pride. They made the room less austere and would serve as a basis for many of my planned room decorations. I was anxious for the children's reaction.

When will I ever learn not to expect the accepted norm from these youngsters? Bible verses finished, I could not restrain my own enthusiasm any longer and asked if they had noticed anything new and unusual. What a mistake!

Alma Yoder, Katie's older sister in the fourth grade, said primly and parrot-like, "We don't believe in adorning our windows with curtains. It's a sign of worldly showiness."

It was little John Henry, the one who all think to be slightly slow who managed to voice the most acute criticism, "Why hide God's world? It's beautiful." All I could think of was "out of the mouth of babes..."

When I arrived in the morning I had been so intent in putting the curtains up before the pupils entered that I forgot about the white envelope I found under the door. It lay on my desk unopened. Just before ten o'clock I sat down at my desk trying to decide which poem the seventh graders should learn this week. They were assigned the project but in the end I knew all the upper grades would be able to recite it. Absentmindedly I opened the letter. It was an invitation.

"Children," I said, still uncertain of their response, "the Southwest school's softball team would like to play us here on Friday, the 29th, should we accept?"

Sheer pandemonium broke loose. There was unbelievable excitement; it was minutes before I could control their exuberance. Even so the air was so saturated with high potency tension, I declared recess time early.

There was no question about acceptance. Southwest was Froggy Bottom's bitter rival and had beaten them savagely last year. It was quite insulting not even to have to bicker over which playing field was to be used; but it was definitely to our advantage to play on our home ground. Daniel was quickly selected to head the team, and he surprisingly became a fair but very demanding coach. Tryouts would be held at noon to choose the ten-member team with two substitutes allowed. The excitement was electric and contagious. The second morning period of arithmetic and geography was today eclipsed by mental images of future Froggy Bottom victors. Usually class problem solving on the blackboard brought the whole school's attention to the front to witness who was the brightest and quickest–not today. Always the pulling down of the map from its high wall cylinder case focused everyone's attention on the exotic unknowns of the world selected by my long wooden pointer. Today it seemed to provide the stimulus for whispered intrigue.

Lunch lasted less than ten minutes. The best players were known and here democracy played no part. Froggy Bottom was out to win. The only unanswered question was who was to be the team's pitcher. Try-outs were held. As much as the boys disliked to admit it, the best without a doubt was Gladys Rohrer; she had an unerring eye and a steady, sure right arm.

By 12:15 p.m. batting practice began. Over and over Chris Yoder and Abner Hostetler batted. They are both heavy hitters whom Daniel was now trying hard to control for in this game as played in the country, over the ditch or fence is out.

Team strategy was thoroughly discussed. It was decided Mary Michael and her brother Aaron would try to find out on Sunday where the weakest point of Southwest's outfield was. They were Holdeman Mennonites and many children of their congregation attended Southwest School.

My desk became the reporting center of the youngest as they had no possible chance of actively participating in this event. This was a revenge game, a game for the honor of Froggy Bottom and to win was very serious business. My only role was to be certain our acceptance was received.

—◆—

Autumn is here. The poplars around the pond are turning golden; the breeze flits with tufts of spent Canadian thistles; brown cattails stand tall and lonely in beds of drooping, dried herbage; maples redden; acorns have fallen from their oak mothers now dressed in rich browns.

This magnificent fall beauty was, however, to be the cause of a crisis in my schoolroom. With Daniel concentrating on Chris and Abner's batting abilities and Gladys acting as pitcher and Omar Hostetler as catcher, the Three Musketeers (Bobby, Charlie and James) momentarily were rather at loose ends.

According to the version which I was told, Bobby had seen a mink in the small stream which feeds into the pond, and he wanted to show his friends the site. Leaving the school grounds without permission is strictly forbidden but they had paid no heed. On the way they saw clumps of colored sumac with beautiful red clusters. James, as the bright and informed one, said sumacs with red fruits were non-poisonous. Now fully realizing the gravity of their position, being absence without leave, they thought that a beautiful bouquet for me might make a nice peace offering. Charlie, the strongest and most adventuresome, climbed up and with his pocketknife cut five or six branches with attached fruit clusters. It was hard work, the day hot and he perspired profusely. On the way back he proudly guarded the prize, but by the time they reached the pond's edge they knew James somehow had been misinformed. Charlie's hands and face were a blotchy red mess of itchy inflammation. He dumped the branches and all ran to the schoolhouse.

My first-aid experience and kit were both woefully inadequate. I was just about to swab the affected areas with alcohol when Dorothy cried, "Stop. That's the worst thing you can do. Alcohol spreads the poison."

Quickly and efficiently, she took over. She gently washed the inflamed parts of Charlie's face, hands and arms with clear water. Then she went to the First-Aid cabinet and took out a cake of heavy duty laundry soap. I had wondered why it was there. She made a thick soapy lather which she applied liberally to all the cleansed areas.

"Let the lather dry. Don't touch it. In three hours we'll repeat the soapy lather. Tomorrow all will be well. No puffy eyes, no itchiness, no redness."

Again, Dorothy had rescued me.

—◆—

Friday seemed to arrive all too soon. *The Gettysburg Address* which I had selected as the passage to be learned for this week proved to be too much for my seventh graders; they are not as capable as my sixth graders. I am almost certain that James B. knows it all already–a small tyke with a big mind–I saw him in full oratorical stance on the top step issuing forth with: "Fourscore and seven years ago our fathers brought forth upon this continent a new nation, conceived in liberty and dedicated to the proposition that all men are created equal. Now we are engaged..." This is where he stopped because he had seen me–but he had already captivated all the younger children. They were silent in rapt attention. James possesses an innate sense of the dramatic.

Friday afternoon is rather a slowdown, cleanup, relaxed period. As I promised, if all lessons were complete I would read out loud after lunch. Dorothy suggested a Nancy Drew book; but for once I did not take her advice, instead I chose Johanna Spyri's *Heidi* and from its initial reception I believe I made a good choice.

The weekly spelling test came next. To stimulate the pupil's interest, which seems to be faltering, I announced annual awards. Beginning next week the name of each speller, according to grade, and each week of the school year will be on a huge wall chart. Those who have a perfect score for the week will receive a gold star, those who miss one word, a silver star, more than that, no star. At the end of the year there will be special prizes for those who have all gold, all silver, and all gold and silver stars.

Just how cleaning the erasers became an honored task, I do not know–it truly is a miserable chore. One beats the eraser against the brick wall of the school all the while choking on chalk dust which then covers the body and clothes plus leaving a distinct rectangular mark of white on the bricks. Yet week-after-week, the pupils vie for this honor– today the third graders won. Each grade participates in the draw (I never have asked Dorothy if the Bishops would approve) but can not be a winner two weeks in a row. I draw the winning slip from Daniel's broad brimmed black hat.

These three little girls in the third grade who have all insisted upon using both their first and middle names–Anna Mae, Norma Jean and Clara Sue–are inseparable. They are so charming and sweet, I call them Froggy Bottom's "Three Graces." They could not have looked more quaint, laden with clean erasers and wearing chalk white faces.

On the way to Goshen, I discussed the plans for the softball game next Friday with Mrs. B. She agreed that I had to provide some refreshments. All Southwest School will be coming–their student body is larger than ours–we will have to expect some forty outsiders as the young fellows who drive the spring wagons with some of their friends will want to stay and watch. Mrs. B. suggested that as Eli was taking a load of Jonathan apples to Foraker's cider mill next week, we would offer sweet cider and cookies. This weekend I could make up some batches of gingersnaps and Mary Wise's oatmeal cookies. We figured out that I should make at least fifteen dozen. But what to do about glasses?

Mrs. B. is always good for a practical answer. Tell all the youngsters to bring a glass or cup and one for a guest. She has at least a couple of dozen old cups and glasses for me to borrow so there should be ample.

—◆—

The weekend proved to be another busy one–certainly without the help of my family I could not have achieved all that I did. I sent Trudie to Trump's Grocery Store with a list–molasses, vinegar, ginger, cloves, cinnamon, marshmallows for the gingersnaps and oatmeal and brown sugar for Mary Wise's recipe. Mother had the basic ingredients–sugar, flour, vanilla, baking powder, etc. which she let me have. Irene went to the Brown's farm for fresh eggs. I had John and Ralph working on the spelling wall chart; Ralph made a handsome wooden frame and John meticulously printed in the names with black China ink and made the weekly divisions. Jennie had to go shopping in town so she picked up the small boxes of tiny gold and silver stars at the paper shop. My helper in making cookies was a rather reluctant recruit, Sister Lou, but as she wanted to borrow my new brown sweater, she had no other choice. Actually everything went well in the kitchen and the gingersnaps in the last minute of baking were topped with a half-sliced marshmallow which melted and which I am certain the children will find "fun."

By Sunday afternoon I was well-ready to return to my flock and Mrs. B.'s warm arms. The buggy bulged with cookie boxes, parcels and the huge wall chart.

Mrs. B. was in a particularly chatty mood. Bessie clopped evenly in no great hurry but steadily forward. The sun was warm as we headed west. For some unknown reason, I asked her if she knew the Martin family.

"Now, that is a story. I am surprised you, with all your curiosity, haven't asked before."

Not knowing quite what she meant, I well knew that I was about to hear all about little James Buchanan and his family.

"Grandmother Rebecca is a Biblical-like matriarch. Her husband, Josiah, has finally been relieved of all his earthly sufferings. Rebecca–and woe be the man or woman who would dare to call her Becky–runs her hundred acre farm with iron rod, no-nonsense efficiency and absolutely brooks no opposition. She and her husband did manage to produce one child, a daughter christened Alicia Anne but always and still called "Baby" although she has long since passed the thirty-five year frontier.

"Not only was Baby pampered, she was so overly protected she knew nothing of the outside world, its evils or dangers. Truly an adorable loving child, saucer-sized blue eyes, tight blonde ringlets, always dressed in white lace, pink ribbons and black patent leather shoes; she was sweet and incredibly unspoiled. Time passed and she grew and budded."

At this point Bessie on her own initiative broke into an uneven jogging trot. After a bit of cajoling, Mrs. B. had the old mare settled down. "Now where was I?"

"Baby was budding."

"Oh, yes. As the story goes a door-to-door book salesman–from the *Encyclopedia Britannica*, I believe–came, bedded, left. Supposedly Baby was eager to show off the farm and once in the barn the soft hay and the still softer Baby proved too much for the poor chap. It was the only time that poor Baby ever had an experience–and she did not even realize she had one–but, the result was little James Buchanan.

"Probably in another community unlike ours of plain people there would have been lots of "talk" and condemnation but not here–except in the beginning there were a few harsh comments about Rebecca. Even if her act had been classified as the most gross of "sins" and truly with Baby she had no idea–she was pure innocence–there had never been ostracizing for any of them. The little boy's life has been completely normal. Not ever does one hear or speak of illegitimacy here. Can you imagine his plight in another place? There is no one crueler than children to children. We, plain people, have our faults and they are many, but we try not to hurt others unjustly. It is written in the Holy Scriptures, 'He that is without sin among you, let him first cast a stone at her.' "

Now Bessie broke into a fast trot–she was nearing home– and there would be no more conversation on this trip.

<u>The last week of the month</u>: Monday began with repeating Bible verses; Tuesday opened by repeating the Lord's Prayer; Wednesday morning we sang, "America the Beautiful"–a pattern and routine were immerging. On this morning I found a quart Mason canning jar filled with a bouquet of golden-rod, silver weed, field clover and huge-headed bright red garden dahlias on my desk. Who brought these? I did not know, nor could I guess. I thanked all.

The week seemed to crawl at a snail's pace–the youngsters were anticipating their ball game and I my first pay check.

Samuel Bontrager is the trustee and a cousin of Eli's. Mrs. B. had telephoned to say we would be there late Friday afternoon. Mrs. B., who is quite a crusader, had heard that because I was an inexperienced woman I would not be paid the regular ninety dollars a month salary that men teachers received. She was willing to go to battle for me; and daughter Agnes would have to wait to come home on Saturday. Each day I admired this woman more.

—◆—

Perhaps the anticipation is more fulfilling than the actual fact. Friday afternoon did come. Southwest School arrived singing and bouncing along in three spring wagons at 2:00 p.m. The horses were quickly unhitched and staked behind the boys' toilet so they would not become excited by all the noise. I met the male teacher, Ephriam Burkholder –a bit stiff, middle-aged and evidently not particularly fond of the opposite sex. Daniel as coach for Froggy Bottom and another big lad from Southwest wasted no time in getting the game underway.

Southwest was up to bat first. There would be seven innings. Gladys stood on the pitcher's mound, proud and defiant, much to the surprise of the Southwest group. Unbelievably, perhaps due to the psychological factor, she fanned three out, one after the other. The sides changed. Chris came up to bat; he carefully planted a ball out in the right field. Here was their weakest player. We made three runs in that inning. This is how the whole afternoon proceeded. Gladys was what they called "hot" and she made no mistakes. The long afternoon finally ended with Froggy Bottom the conquering team with a count of seventeen to Southwest's five. The cider and cookies were relished by all. The spring wagons of Southwest left much less bouncily than they had arrived, and my flock of twenty-five–from Daniel to little Norman–were grins from ear-to-ear.

Right on schedule Mrs. B. arrived and we went jolting off to see Cousin Samuel. No matter how strong he might be, if there were to be any question about my paycheck, I had the utmost confidence in Mrs. Maude Bontrager's capacity to achieve her goal. Actually there apparently was never to be a question of money for my check was all prepared, and Mr. Samuel Bontrager could not have been more gentlemanly in his conduct. Or was all this because he, too, had heard the rumor that Cousin Maude was about to launch a battle; and he knew before it began who the winner would be?

This was the end of my first month of teaching at Froggy Bottom. Probably–no, there is no doubt–I, the teacher, have learned more than any of my pupils during this period.

OCTOBER

Tangy bright days–it is a joy to walk to school. The morning freshness brings the blood rushing to the cheeks.

Both Mrs. B. and Dorothy have forewarned me that this month will be a very busy one on the farm and many of my children will be absent as they have to help with the work.

Everyone is predicting a long, hard winter ahead. Much of this impression is based on the groundhog or woodchuck's fat and the frenzied and busy activity of the chipmunks and gophers. In late September the groundhogs seemed to be extra fat and already they have burrowed in for their winter sleep; the little chipmunks and gophers, too, are very fat this year but they unlike the woodchucks keep stores of roots, seeds and berries in their winter quarters for an occasional feast. All this has been related to me by the eloquent James Buchanan who evidently has turned his interest from botany to biology.

"Yesiree, Miss Todd, this is going to be a big long one. Has anybody ever seen these four-legged winter sleepers so fat?"

Although I had been told absenteeism would be high. I was not prepared for my schoolroom this morning. I had eleven pupils in total–the two Knoxs (Norman and Vilma),

John Henry Bender and Susie Cripe, all my three third graders and all four sixth graders.

When I verbally voiced my surprise by asking, "What could my wee little first and second graders–Amos, Katie, Emma and Sadie–be doing to help?"

I was snappily informed by Norman of the first grade, "They're pickin' up spuds. My ma said maybe I could earn money doin' the same."

Potatoes have always been an Indiana staple. As my own Mother often said, "Even at five dollars a bushel, they still would be cheap food." Potatoes in various forms–fried, mashed, boiled–are to be found on the farm family's table three times a day for breakfast, dinner and supper.

Taking advantage of my lightened schedule, I sat down beside Vilma to help her learn the multiplication tables–she is having difficulty. The whispering around us suddenly reached a marked crescendo. As usual it was due to my sixth grade boys. Each and everyone of them have spent long periods standing with their face in the corner as punishment; but whispering still is my biggest and most unsuccessfully controlled disciplinary problem.

"Which one of the three of you would like to explain to the rest of us this paper you are passing around?"

James popped up, "I would be delighted to do so, Miss Todd–that is if you would permit me to illustrate my drawing on the blackboard."

This youngster is always managing to retain the upper hand but I could not help but smile–the blackboard is never allowed to be used by the children for so-called entertainment.

"Draw away, James."

Quickly and very adeptly he drew a hill with a plain vertical side featuring an open-faced doorway and a slotted interior.

"This is supposed to be Willie Ramer's new underground potato cellar he's making."

Then like a little professor, James began his explanation. "To support the sides on the inside he used sturdy logs within the hill; the whole framed area is approximately 16 x 20 feet which certainly can hold up to over a thousand bushels. This means that the hill's interior had to be very strong as potatoes weigh approximately 48-50 pounds per bushel. The roof was first covered with dried brush, then a layer of straw and on top of this a well-rounded layer of earth so as to help the water run off. Any questions?"

"Do most families have such big underground cellars?" I could not help but ask.

"No. They have much smaller cellars both for fruits and vegetables. My guess is that Willie is planning some sort of commercial venture."

"Thank you, James. For once you boys were not just 'hossing around' as you put it."

That evening I helped Mrs. B. peel apples. Eli had bought her a full-sized drier last year for Christmas. Gifts are always practical among the country people. It fits over the top of her wood range in the kitchen, being about three and one-half feet long and two feet wide. The drier is made with a two and one-half inch upright tin frame; one inch of the base is for water and it has a steam vent in the left hand corner and is covered with a thin sheet of tin over which are spread the apple slices. Mrs. B. is very proud of her drier as she is one of the few women in the community to have one. Others are still spreading their sliced apples out on their roofs for the sun to dry. So they must dry in late

August and early September when the sun is still hot but when the apples are not so good and ripe. These dried apples, which every country child of all ages loves to nibble on at any time, are called by their "Pennsylvania Dutch" name, *apfel snitz.*

Potatoes came up again during our apple paring and slicing conversation. Mrs. B. told me potato digging when it is just for the family is considered the work for women and children. Mamma digs the potato hills out with a pitch fork and dumps them on the ground. The smaller children wipe them clean and put them into buckets or a child's wagon if they are fortunate enough to have one; older children then spread them out on the barn floor for 'curing' as this drying out is called. Later the potatoes will be put into the underground bins or cellars.

It was nearly ten o'clock and we still had a half-bushel to finish–as we both noted women's work is never done.

"Nor her talk," was Mr. B.'s comment as he took himself to bed.

"Our menfolk also work long and hard," his wife commented and stressed with a wily smile, "and eat heartily."

Mrs. B. adroitly popped a slice of Jonathan apple into her mouth, "Apples are also a preferred fruit–most everybody here has their own orchard–and never is there a table set without bread, butter and a jar of good thick applebutter. Wait 'til you taste Grandma Mast's. She makes the best."

As we were finally clearing up, Mrs. B. causally said, "Why don't you stay here this weekend? Go visit some of your pupils. See their homes and countryside. You can drive Bessie and the spring wagon. I'll let you use the telephone to call your ma."

Almost as a seeming afterthought she added, "Besides Agnes is going to take the train to Elkhart to visit her cousin."

Not that I had any choice. Mrs. B. had her plans already well in place and driving into Goshen on Friday afternoon was not one of them–but I also was looking forward to seeing the home ambiance of some of my charges.

On Friday, Dorothy reappeared and with her came an invitation to watch and help her grandmother make applebutter on Saturday. That very morning Mrs. B. told me I could use Bessie Saturday morning until noon; so I accepted but with the distinct impression that I was a manipulated pawn.

Before dismissing school for the week, I bent over Orval's desk and whispered in his ear, "Monday I want you to recite a new Bible verse. You quoted 'Jesus wept' for the past four weeks."

Saturday morning I bounced out of Agnes' big double bed–I have learned country people do not make nor buy single beds; for cost purposes, a double is more reasonable and practical. Agnes has a beautiful pink and white china wash pitcher and bowl which I am allowed to use. On school mornings, I fill the pitcher with hot water from the reservoir attached to the kitchen range. Today I splashed in cold water for I did not want to waste any more time. I grabbed a heavy coat sweater and a brown knit stocking cap. Bessie had to be harnessed but Mrs. B. insisted I eat my breakfast of fried eggs and potatoes, ham and coffee. I probably hurt her feelings but simply could not eat a piece of crumb cake. Gently I reminded her I did not need to eat as much as a man.

God bless him! Mr. B. had gone out and readied Bessie for me. The mare seemed as excited as I was. Her step was high and light. The morning dew glistened on the long roadside grasses. I could see my breath and Bessie's. It was snappy cold. The small gravel stones click-clacked rhythmically against the metal rims of the wheels as we clopped along. Up and down, left then left again, after another mile we entered a narrower sandy road, its center sparsely green. This lovely and lonely track wound through alfalfa stubble which already had begun to take on its color of winter green. With clear overhead skies and no one to hear but old Bessie I began to recite out loud, "When the frost is on the punkin and the fodder's in the shock..." Bessie's appreciation of James Whitcomb Riley was apparently limited as she quickened her pace on the downgrade and we swung sharply to the right to enter an even narrower and little used pathway. High on the hill in the distant under a huge elm stood a waiting Dorothy. When she saw us she began to wave frantically. To my utter dismay she was wearing a vivid, solid orange dress. She flew down the hill, her big bare feet instinctively avoiding all endangering obstacles. Climbing in beside me Dorothy fairly bubbled with pride.

"Like it?" she asked as she fingered the coarse cotton. "Grandma made it–suffering all the time–she allows my 'English' blood comin' out. As I am not yet of marrying age, this once she granted my waywardness."

At the very top lay a low sprawling house, unpainted and weathered. A long wide porch covered three sides; we climbed its wooden steps when Dorothy stopped, "Look!"

I turned. Below the valley hung heavy with morning haze, the soft light muted the colors, the sound of deep silence reigned. It was as if a pristine page of a past age had been opened for us to view. It was an incredibly beautiful scene.

Potted plants in painted tins and sturdy wooden rockers enhanced the porch's simple elegance. Before entering the house Dorothy took my hand and pulled me to the far side. Just below the slight slope was a cultivated rectangle of precise greens and browns framed in a blaze of color.

"Grandma's garden."

In the center were plumb-lined straight rows of still existing vegetables–carrots, cabbage, turnips, onions, beets, parsnips, potatoes. But it was the brilliant border which caught and held the eye–asters, dahlias, zinnias, all sizes and shades of marigolds (yellow, oranges, ambers) stalks of tall, straight hollyhocks and low, showy multi-color phlox.

"We Amish are not supposed to have much to do with decoration. Grandma loves beauty–and flowers are God's way of ornamentin'–so they ain't no sin."

Inside the one big room, the immediate impression was of immaculate starkness. The wide floor planks appeared scoured with lye; the window panes sparkled with sun stars; the rectangular wooden table was surrounded by four straight-backed wooden chairs; a small brick-faced fire place, neat, blackened and cold, was on the north wall.

Grandmother Mast stood on one of the scattered braided rugs in the center of the room. It was a formal, almost stiff introduction. I was slightly taken aback, but then I realized the old woman spoke little English.

Again Dorothy took charge. She wanted to show me her Grandmother's hutch. Behind closed glass doors I saw a remarkable unscarred collection of Gaudy Dutch china– deep blues, bright orange to red, tipped in gold. It was a very complete set–plates, cups and saucers, bowls, pitchers–all were in mint condition. These distinctly spoke of another way of life.

"I told you Grandma liked beautiful things." Her quick eye read my face and she whispered, "My grandparents used to be very rich with big farms on the other side of Middlebury–but my Mother's wild shenanigans–her debts which they had to pay caused Grandma and Grandpa to lose everything."

Amish fashion Grandma Mast's head was covered with a white cotton pleated cap with two loose ties; her long dress and matching over-apron were in plain dark gray caught in back by a small brustle-like gathering. Below her heavy skirts were a few inches of black cotton stockings and flat-soled, laced black shoes.

Her face, which the rays of the sun had never touched, was fair and a reminder of peachy youth still colored cherubic cheeks, but the furrows of sadness and perhaps toil had been etched deep. A rim of white hair edged her equally white covering. Once it undoubtedly had been very blonde as her eyes were still a very brilliant blue.

"*Dorsee, cum.*" The rotund woman waved gaily for us to follow her. With these words, their tone and her gesture, I knew I was not unwelcome.

Outside between the garden and a low hanging willow tree, with a view of the valley, a fire of apple wood had been carefully prepared. The embers were hot and low. An enormous blackened kettle and its rack stood aside in readiness.

"Grandma told me to explain everything. Last night, 'cause you were comin' we peeled, cored, and quartered nearly two bushels of apples, Jonathans and Winesaps. Grandma don't cook by measure, only feel."

The rack and kettle–its interior a glistening copper sheen–were now placed over the fire and the prepared apples dumped in.

"Now, comes the apple cider."

Jug after jug was poured over the apples. "You've gotta well cover the apples—then begin to stir, slowly, slowly, but never stop."

Grandma Mast now had a long-handled wooden paddle which she constantly turned in an even, never-changing rhythm.

"Stirring goes on 'til the mixture comes to a boil. When the apples turn to pulp, the sugar and cinnamon are added."

The applebutter-making had begun around 8:30 a.m. By ten o'clock the sweetening and flavoring ingredients were stirred in. Quantities were a bit nebulous, somewhere around ten pounds of sugar and three huge fistfuls of cinnamon went into the bubbling kettle.

"The right thickness and color only Grandma can gage."

It was so peaceful that no one seemed to mind the passing of time. I sat on a low stool and was mesmerized by the countryside. For minutes I watched a circling hawk, sometimes gracefully buoyed on an air current, another time voluntarily swooping in quest of his frightened prey.

Grandma had also been watching. Never stopping her stirring, she spoke slowly. Dorothy translated.

"Beautiful. Cruel and dangerous as beautiful creatures often are."

In time Dorothy added more of her Grandmother's words, "The longer you stir, the more taste—and love—you put into your applebutter."

By 11:30 a.m. Dorothy had finished ladling the thick amber-brown paste into heavy eathernware crockery—only Grandma knew the real secrets of applebutter-making.

Settled behind Bessie, Grandma grasped my hand in farewell, "Come again if you're here sometime."

I repeated these lovely words often on the way back to the Bontragers. Lesson of the day–there is much more to applebutter-making than the adding of cider, sugar and cinnamon.

— ♦ —

Monday morning came and I was anticipating hearing the Bible verses recited. I wondered if Orval would openly disobey and repeat his usual two-worder.

When his time came, he carefully stood and gave a long pause before saying, "Be ye careful not to kick over the bucket when it 'tis full of milk." He then looked me directly in the eye and serenely added, "Jonathan 1:1."

Again there were few of my upper class students present. I rather causally commented that we were never going to complete our year's educational program if the students did not attend classes. Orval, whose mother had sent him unwillingly to school today, almost shouted.

"You know most schools have a two-week holiday during corn huskin' time?"

Although I did not believe it at the time (Mrs. B. confirmed it later), I was fully aware that everyone in the room was restless and felt as if they were missing a good time.

My two fifth grade boys were particularly agitated. Aaron and Omar both had an older brother and sister who had stayed at home to work. Talking about it I thought might help–besides, I, too, wanted to learn what went into this celebrated farm work.

With so few students present it would be an opportune time to commence our public speaking program. The fifth graders were told to prepare a piece on the corn husking season. I placed three chairs on the platform where I had them all sit. Each speaker in turn was formally introduced to their slightly amused but respectful audience.

Vilma began first. Almost verbatim from our World Book, she explained all about corn being discovered here in the Americas and its being a principal crop in the state of Indiana.

After this historical background, the boys' turns came, each giving their presentation their own set of practicalities.

"Big A, little a, r-o-n, that's my name. Today I am to speak to you about corn huskin'. How it is done.

"A flat bottomed hay wagon with the sides on is driven into the corn field. Normally there are three huskers to a wagon. Everybody takes a row on the right side of the wagon, throwing the husked corn into the wagon and tellin' the horse when to start and stop. Some families have a boy like me, or younger, drive the horse. Some families share the work with other families. Some work jist with their own family. If you work out and are paid you can earn good money. A good husker can bring in ninety bushels a day. Wages today are six cents a bushel. That puts over five dollars in a fella's pocket! Guess that's about all I got to say—'cept the womenfolk always get together and cook extra special during these days."

Omar was next. He began without preamble.

"Corn husking is an art. The modern way of doin' it is to use a hook which is in the middle of a metal frame which is set in leather to protect the hand and strapped to the right hand. The husk is ripped aside and the corn is stripped as clean as possible of husk and hair. A good husker leaves a clean ear. Do you want me to draw a picture?"

After James' blackboard victory of the other day, I shook my head negatively.

"Children, let's give these three excellent speakers a big round of applause. The first public speakers from Froggy Bottom!"

Perhaps the plaudits from their schoolmates took away some of the fifth graders' disappointment in not sharing in the corn husking season. At least everyone had something new to talk about.

— ♦ —

The days pass–the calendar pages flipped by the 15th– I had been teaching Vilma (fifth) and Gladys (sixth) how to knit. One day at noon while at my desk, the three cherubs from the third grade approached, almost on tip-toe.

Norma Jean in the center finally stammered out, "Miss Todd, would you please teach us to knit, too?"

Everyone here is always so eager to learn something new and different–it makes teaching a pleasure.

That same afternoon I was still working at my desk; this week report cards are due. I was working on James B. Martin's card. Handwriting, 'letter-copying' as the children call it, is taught only in the first three grades but James' handwriting at times is so illegible that I warned him if he were not more careful he would have to take lessons again with the third graders. "Didn't he want to be successful in life?" had been my unwise question. To which he retorted, "I will be–and I will have a secretary to do my writing for me."

At this point in my mental rummaging, in popped a disheveled Dorothy handing me a fistful of bright orange bittersweet vines.

"They are still green–they have to dry but they will last all winter. Grandma told me to pick them for you–the whole south-line fence is covered with them."

Dorothy was in a particularly chatty mood but I had known her long enough to know what she was talking about was not what she had come to say.

While I waited, I thanked her for the privilege of meeting her Grandmother and for the morning of applebutter-making.

"Usually applebutter time is for a big gathering. Everybody comes–lots of children running around and women sitting, peeling, talking and stirring–a big production. Mrs. Bontrager thought it better to start you slow and easy."

I smiled. The forces working behind the scene are carried foreword on well-greased wheels. Mrs. B. truly was a first-class organizer.

Dorothy's declaration finally came. "Miss Todd, I know it is early to be sayin' this–but, at the end of the year hardly anybody–almost never–doesn't pass on with his grade–some of us are jist more fast than others–the Bishops..."

I had learned when Dorothy needed to add impetus to any of her arguments she invoked the omnipotence of the Bishops.

"...consider it an experience goin' to school and we should not be punished by bein' divided 'cause God did not make us all the same; we are not all equal no matter what the Constitution and the Declaration of Dependence says. I knew you'd be fixin' our first report cards–so I thought I'd let you know."

—◆—

The beautiful autumn days, crisp and snappy, abruptly changed. Overnight the bright colorful world was turned into a deaden study of lifeless brown–it had been a killing frost.

"Squaw's Winter that's what we call it," Dorothy informed me. "Glad you got to see Grandma's garden before she descended. These cold days won't last–it ain't winter time yet."

Again the Amish girl proved to be right. Soon after, there was again another shift in the weather. The skies became incredibly clear and celestial blue. A musty odor of past summer floated in on buoyant winds. Warmth shrouded the few remaining vibrant colors of autumn in soft smoky haze.

"Now these days we call Indian Summer–glorious ain't they?" Dorothy had again shed her shoes. "They're like trumpets–they announce that the bleak, cold days of winter are near-at-hand."

These last days of fall beauty actually precipitated my first moral crisis among the children. In the morning the pupils all arrive promptly but in the late afternoon some who do not have pressing chores dawdle going home.

To be exact it was four of the dawdlers–Bobby Hartman, Charlie Weaver, Gladys Rohrer and little John Henry Bender–who caused the school to be divided into "takers" and "thieves."

One morning I was still sweeping the front steps after ringing the first bell when a wee voice behind me said, "Miss Todd, is it stealin' to take an apple if you're hungry?"

Turning around I was to see a very trouble-faced John Henry. Without question there was a serious problem at hand.

"Let's go in. We'll sit down and talk."

Soon I was to learn the three cowboys–Bobby, Charlie and Gladys (sex plays no role here)–with their camp's cook, John Henry, were daily riding off along the western trail in a cloud of dust on fast imaginary horses. The journey was hard and arduous and made more so with marauding Indians behind every tree. These four were bound to get "extra hungry" especially about the time they were passing the Mishler orchard where apples were heaped in piles under trees in readiness for collection. Being in charge of the camp's "grub," it was John Henry's job to crawl in on his belly and bring back apples for his "pardners."

Analyzing the situation, I decided this was a problem to be brought to the attention of all the pupils. That morning I began the day with the facts as I knew them from John Henry. An open discussion followed.

Daniel, as would be expected, responded immediately, "Thou shalt not steal is one of our Ten Commandments. It is wrong to steal these apples and particularly for the older ones to send in an innocent younger child."

Also to be expected, it was James next taking the floor, first to defend his classmates, and then just for the fun of contradiction. "Is this stealing? Was there a fence enclosing this orchard? No. Would it not be possible for an animal to snatch or a bird to peck at these apples? Would you have these tiny creatures of the wild condemned for following the laws of Nature? No, of course not. Then, why deny a hungry child?"

If James B. does not become a lawyer, he has missed his calling–he truly is a brilliant little boy.

Daniel may not be fluid with words as James but he, too, made his points, "It is also written 'even a child is known by his doings...' The things we do today speak of the kind of men and women we will be tomorrow."

James again bounced up. He in the meantime had asked to use the Bible and now with his finger in between the pages, he stood, small and straight, all he needed was a black frock coat to complete his demeanor.

"I can not compete with Daniel on his knowledge of our Holy Scriptures, but let me read you Matthew 6:19. 'Lay not up for yourselves treasure upon earth, where moth and rust doth corrupt and where thieves break through and steal.' "

The basic knowledge these youngsters have of the Bible is amazing.

"Now, why should Farmer Mishler have piles of apples heaped up, perhaps rotting–and remember with no fence around so thieves do not have to break through and steal. This is in itself like an offering–a gift to a passing hungry child–it is not stealing..."

Daniel broke in, "As always my friend James manages to thoroughly cloud the basic question. Again I say, it is wrong. 'Thou shalt not steal' is a commandment! I will also add, it is written 'stolen waters are sweet and bread eaten in secret is pleasant' but that does not in any way say stealing is right in the eyes of the Lord."

James smiled naughtily, "Daniel, is it also not written '...comfort me with apples...'?"

I decided to intervene. These two could continue this parlance for hours.

"Children, I believe that none of us should trespass on property which is not ours–that is, without permission. So in the future Farmer Mishler's orchard is not to be entered unless you are invited to do so. May I also add, never ask anyone do something that you would not do yourself, no matter what his or her age. As for the questions of taking or stealing, this all of you will have to answer within your own hearts."

As I finished I could not help wondering if I had been strong enough in my statement. Time will tell when we see the kind of men and women who will immerge from Froggy Bottom.

—◆—

The children are completely unaccustomed to having the schoolroom decorated. Draping strips of orange crepe paper across the top of the blackboard and cutting out black cats and witches on broomsticks to pin on the curtains are done with a certain tolerance for this city slicker teacher's queer ways.

When I asked if there was any way I could get some corn shocks and pumpkins before the Halloween party, I felt an absolute questioning surprise in the eyes of all present. No one answered. I went on to say jack-o'-lanterns were made from pumpkins by cutting out a mouth, nose and eyes in the shell and placing a candle inside the cleaned-out pumpkin.

Finally bright-eyed Susie Cripe (second-grade), raised her hand, "What do you do at the party?"

Could it be these children did not know about Halloween? "We play games like pin-the-tail on the donkey–the person is blindfolded–and bob for apples."

Again I felt the need to offer an explanation, "The apples are in a tub of water–the person has to kneel down with his hands behind his back and try to bite into an apple with his mouth. Besides apples, we will have carmel popcorn balls, nuts and cider to eat and drink." Instinctively I knew no one here would wear masks nor dress up in costumes.

Mary Michael (seventh grade), who I still know little about, said somberly, "Here, in the country we think it is sinful to waste. I'll ask Ma to give me a cleaned-out pumpkin."

The next morning when I arrived, outside the schoolhouse's double doors stood three corn shocks (all ears removed) with five pumpkin shells at their base. Gradually we are becoming acquainted with each other.

It was nearing the end of the month and regularity had returned to the schoolroom. Tardiness is not usual among the pupils. Today Amos (first grade) came in a whole fifteen minutes late, smelling distinctly of cow manure.

When questioned he haltingly answered in his newly acquired English, "The Jersey cow don't give down so good for Papa."

Dorothy finished my mental groping before taking him to the pump, "His hands are small–probably the cow's teats are sore–so he has to milk her."

— ♦ —

Wednesday it is usual to begin the day with group singing. Today at recess time, after a particularly woeful off-key performance this morning, my three big girls, Grace, Mary and Dorothy, came to me to say it was time to start learning some new songs for the Christmas program.

When I asked if they had any suggestions, I could feel they wanted to say something else.

Finally Grace said, "We think it might be better if I taught the new songs."

Mary added, "Grace has a lovely voice. She helps with the singing in her church."

My non-tonal voice must have been most disturbing to them. Smiling and inwardly relieved, I suggested they be the committee for song selection, and Grace act as the school's new song-mistress.

Music, in the form of singing, plays a major role in country life. As musical instruments are rare–the Amish do not permit them at all–voices are strong and vibrant. All pride themselves on their ability to read and sing music well.

This all according to Mrs. B., who further added, "Our Wednesday night prayer meetings and our Sunday church services are to be heard to be believed. Our song leader, Rueben Miller's wife, Elsie, an alto–she can lead us all into fervent rejoicing with our hymn-singing."

The end of the month came with a comical incident. All my Amish boys, little Amos, Orval and big Daniel, appeared with their bangs cut. On each face there was at least a two-inch strip of white above their still tanned cheeks.

As Dorothy matter-of-factly put it, "Winter is settin' in–the boys have had their pre-snow haircuts."

NOVEMBER

"Got to be hot right off the griddle," Mrs. B. said to me as I sipped my morning coffee. Her face was rosy red from the range's intense heat, "And fried crisp." She was flipping the mush rectangles with a practiced hand but stopped in mid-air when she heard the telephone ring.

The bell of the telephone instills a certain fear. Mrs. B. ran to answer, then she turned white-faced to me.

"It's for you."

My heart, too, filled with trepidation. Who could be calling me at this hour? Something must have happened at home. The wooden telephone box hung high on the wall and as I reached to pick up the black trumpet-like receiver, I supported my right hand on its writing shelf. In the far distance I heard my mother's voice to which I responded.

"Tell Dad to pick me up right after school today. I'll be all ready to go home then."

"Real bad, child?"

"No. Actually it's something I've always wanted to do. I've been chosen to sit on our local election board."

"You ain't old enough."

"Not really, but as a teacher I qualify."

Without hesitation I had accepted. One does not waste time in small talk on the telephone–they are instruments for emergencies.

Before school took up that morning, I noticed a huddle of older girls and I thought I heard Gladys say, "There won't be any tomorrow–you wait and see."

Immediately after opening session, I announced tomorrow there would be no school as I had been chosen to serve as a member of the local Election Board in my community. To which there was never a mutter, murmur, or question, only a hoarse whisper from Gladys, "What did I tell you?"

At recess time I called Gladys to my desk, "How did you know there would be no school tomorrow?"

"Ma heard it over the telephone."

"You mean she listened in on the line? She listened to my conversation?"

"Sure. How else would anybody know what's goin' on?"

My father arrived a little before 3:30 p.m. and parked at the foot of the steps in his newly purchased Model T Ford. When school let out all the boys circled, petted and peered in at this shiny black novelty. Both man and boys were beaming.

"A brand new 1922–how much did it cost?"

This was straight men's talk.

"Two hundred and ninety-five dollars."

My grandmother bought one of the first Model T's– 1909–for nine hundred and fifty dollars." said James. "She's still driving it."

"How come the price come down so much?" asked Bobby. "Ain't the car so good anymore?"

That was the question which launched the repartee between my Father and James.

"Son, they are better—it's all due to Mr. Ford's new management policies."

Dad was a personal admirer of Henry Ford and was a staunch Indiana supporter for him to enter national politics.

"First of all he believes the product, in this case, his Model T, must fit the needs of the people in quality and price—so what did he do? In 1914, only eight years ago, he increased the wages of his workers to a minimum of five dollars for an eight-hour working day. As his workmen became more trained, their pay increases to as much as six or seven dollars a day. This skilled labor in turn stimulated production..."

James could stand it no longer. He burst in with, "Increased production and more car sales brought the prices down."

"That's absolutely right, Sonny."

Again James, who was not about to relinquish his conversational toe-hold, went on with, "Do you know they got continuously moving work lines in the River Rouge plant in Michigan?"

Dad also liked his place on the platform, and Mr. Ford and his car models were one of his favorite topics. "Those are called assembly lines—another innovation of Henry Ford. It is his belief that the work should go to the man and not the man to the work."

Here I interrupted or we would not get home before dark. Dad cranked up his prize, the motor sputtered and after three turns, he jumped in and we bolted forth jerkily. Dad has yet to conquer the shifting of gears. I looked back and waved. My youngsters still stood on the steps in complete awe of this thoroughly modern schoolteacher of theirs.

Election Day, the first Tuesday after the first Monday in November, and my personal day of glory passed. The next day, Wednesday, I was back in school where everything resumed as if nothing had occurred.

Before bringing my recent experience with voting rights and obligation of the citizen before the seventh grade civics class for discussion–it must always be remembered, like the telephone, everyone in a one-room school listens in to any subject that may catch their attention–I wanted Mrs. B.'s opinion. It was my impression that government in most any form is not looked upon with too much favor here in the community.

When asked, Mrs. B. who had been washing dishes in the dishpan, took up her apron and slowly began to dry her hands.

"Difficult to say. How one looks at government is pretty much decided by where you stand in religion–Mennonite or Amish–not that either of us is strong to get involved.

"My people, the Mennonites, recognize that there must be a government–to punish evil and protect the good." Mrs. B. was still drying her hands.

"The Amish are much more rigid–they do not believe in the government having any rights over the individual's spiritual world–an individual is responsible only to God. They are forbidden to take an oath–they are not allowed to participate in any kind of political activity. Dear-oh-me, this is too weighty a subject–why don't you ask Daniel? He is studying to become a deacon and some day sure he will be a bishop."

As always Mrs. B.'s suggestion had merit. I asked Daniel to speak on Amish views on voting and participation in government. I could see he was genuinely pleased, but he said he would need some time for preparation.

Came the day for Daniel's presentation and as might have been expected it was very formal. Should the setting have been different Daniel could have been addressing a congregation; he even wore his Sunday frock coat.

"We Amish are law-abiding citizens–rarely are our people involved in criminal actions. Our attitude toward government dates back to our Swiss forefathers in the 16th century. Then, as now, we respect the State and think it un-Christian to oppose its function to maintain order other than when it breaks God's laws. Then, rather than fighting or open rebellion, it has been our history to leave if possible, or tolerate if impossible.

"Our people do not run for political offices nor participate in any of their activities. These spheres can lead to force and violence which are against our belief. I just read the following in the Farm Bureau paper that a man called Mahatma Gandhi said in his defense against charges of sedition, 'Nonviolence is the first article of my faith. It is also the last article of my creed.' His are brave words, but it sums up very well the way the Amish people think and believe.

"Our people do not settle disputes in courts of law either among ourselves or with outsiders–nor do we serve on juries. It is written 'Judge not, that ye be not judged.'

"Contrary to the thoughts of many, we are allowed by our faith to vote. Probably we are most concerned with local rather than national elections as it is our policy to vote for the person we know and trust rather than the party. Although many are not registered–once we are recorded, we usually vote regularly. Because we are a conservative group, most of our members belong to the Republican Party.

"Thank you for listening. God bless you all."

What else could I have expected from shy and sweet Daniel? He probably will not say another word for the rest of the month.

When Friday afternoon came around, I announced that we would have to make up the day we lost so there was to be school on Saturday. There was not one complaint nor objection. My authority in the schoolroom is unquestioned!

—◆—

November 11th, Armistice Day is approaching. It has been four years since the end of the World War. It played an integral part in my adolescent years. As a young teenager, I had been very patriotic devoting many hours to war work. I rolled yards and yards of bandages and knitted hundreds of gauntlets–long thick gloves which left the finger-tips free (the yarn was supplied by the Red Cross). Within each pair, I usually tucked a letter.

Often I received a "thank you" from a lonely Yank and a correspondence sprang up sometimes with a photograph of a smiling lad in uniform enclosed. I still have all these letters including some of mine, returned, unopened and stamped in red "unclaimed" on the envelope. They are tied together with a blue satin ribbon. I can not destroy them for perhaps these may be the only remembrance left of those unsung young who so tragically gave their hardly begun lives.

They had become close and very personal to me. Unshed tears still well deep in my heart. I can not forget those young men who will never return.

Yet, I know that many in this community, the parents and brothers of the students of Froggy Bottom, do not believe in war or sending their young men to fight. Most of the young men in this community were deferred to work on the farms, but their religion demanded that they be classified as conscientious objectors.

There are twenty-three states which observe Armistice Day as a legal holiday, but Indiana is not one of them. Without saying anything to Mrs. B., as I was uncertain if the question of the War would also be too sensitive for her, I decided to tell the children that we would be celebrating Armistice Day with two minutes of silence as it is observed in England. Should anyone so wish they may contribute their words on this occasion.

On November 11th at 11 a.m., I had all the children stand, put their hands to their hearts, bow their heads and close their eyes.

"On this day in 1918," I said, "the Armistice to end all wars was signed between the Allies and Germany. Let it be so—so that those who gave their lives will not have died in vain."

After two minutes of silence, I asked if anyone wished to express any thoughts. To my utter astonishment, Grace said, "I would like to sing 'The Star-Spangled Banner.'"

The girl has a lovely voice. My knowledge of music is very limited, but I believe hers should be professionally trained. Our national anthem is extremely difficult to sing, and Grace soared to its musical heights clearly and without hesitation.

When she finished, a bedraggled Vilma raised her hand, "I should like to read 'Trees'—I had hoped to know it," (the fifth graders are learning this poem) "but it is too beautiful to spoil. Sergeant Joyce Kilmer who wrote it was an infantryman who was killed in France on July 30, 1918."

Then she began slowly, "I think that I shall never see..." The only extraneous sound in the room was the harsh wind pelting against the window panes—the tomb-like silence continued until she closed with "But only God can make a tree."

Another hand was raised. Mary Michael was also a most unexpected participant.

"I, too, should like to read a poem written by an officer, Lieutenant-Colonel John McCrae who died in France in 1918 after serving on the western front for four years. His poem, 'In Flanders Fields' is powerfully sad–and beautiful."

She then began, "In Flanders fields the poppies blow...."

Even this was not all. Next was James who was hardly unexpected. He stood upright with book in hand. Although I have no proof, I have a very strong premonition that he somehow has had a hand in the orchestration of this entire program.

"I, too, should like to read a poem which I believe was the greatest to come out of the World War–and like the others heard today, Alan Seeger, the poet was killed. Ironically his death occurred on the day of our national Independence, July 4th, in the year 1916. He entitled his poem, 'I Have a Rendezvous with Death.' "

James never once looked at the page. He recited the poem with the passion and feeling of a trained performer.

As he recited the last line of the poem, "I shall not fail that rendezvous," Grace began singing the hauntingly beautiful "Going Home" in a full-throated mature voice.

Tears unabashedly streamed down my face and little Sadie Smucker came over and touched my hands, "Don't cry, Miss Todd. They're all in Heaven."

I shall never forget Armistice Day, 1922. It was one of the most beautiful acts of loving children that one could imagine. Again these young hearts taught me a great lesson.

The days of November are gray and the heavy dark clouds speak of pending snow; the winds are sharp and blustery but within the schoolroom there is a universal spirit of congeniality and productivity.

On the weekend I brought back modeling clay. Often I feel that I devote much more time and interest to my pupils in the upper classes. This was to be used by the first two grades. I told them they could make whatever they wanted. They were completely absorbed for hours. Making mid-morning rounds, I asked each in turn what was his creation.

I began with the first grade. Norman proudly replied, "A car." Amos looked up and softly and rather sheepishly said, "A scooter." And little Katie sweetly cooed, "A doll."

On to the second grade, Emma forthrightly said, "A rocking chair." Sadie, "I think it's goin' to be a cow—maybe a horse." Susie was well on the way to making a very discernible "kitten."

Lastly was John Henry, working busily and completely engrossed. I stood by his desk and saw neat rows of molded mounds. When I asked him what these were, he answered with a look and tone of utter disbelief at my ignorance, "Tombstones!"

My theory of discovering more about the inner child through his creative work went out the window with John Henry. I was completely and thoroughly baffled, but then J.H. never fits any pattern it would seem.

—◆—

November is the month of the Pilgrims, Thanksgiving and Longfellow. Room decoration which had been so unknown to these children before is now part of Art. My third-graders are incredibly creative. Tracing, drawing and snipping out of colored construction paper, these three furnished all the black cutout Pilgrim figures and brown red-headed turkeys for our curtains.

One of the discoveries made during these days was my seventh grader Abner Hostetler's artistic talent. I mentioned I wished I could have a copy of the *Mayflower* to put on our blackboard. I actually was thinking of a photograph. When he offered to draw one for me, I was most skeptical as I well knew how much the children loved to use the blackboard. I did give him chalk and told him to draw only on the section directly behind my desk, and I went on teaching fifth grade literature. This month we are reading Longfellow's "*Hiawatha*." The children dearly love this poem. I believe half of the pupils know many lines 'by heart' as they say, for when we recite, "By the shores of Gitche Gumee, by the shining Big-Sea-Water, stood the wigwam of Nokomis..." there seems to be a roomful of verbal participation.

Today's recitation period was longer than usual, and I had quite forgotten about Abner who had returned to his seat in the meantime. I could not have been more astounded by what I saw. An exact replica of the *Mayflower* centered the section with the coastline of England serving as a misty background and a Pilgrim couple about to descend upon Plymouth Rock in the foreground.

"Abner, it is wonderful–you are really talented!" The boy blushed rosy-red and cast his eyes downward. "You are Froggy Bottom's Michelangelo."

—◆—

Today a few snow flurries scurried around. This month has brought some minor changes to our daily routine. The boys, big and small, with Daniel acting as job supervisor have taken over the outside chores. This month, Omar and Aaron bring in the wood for the stove. Chris and Abner are in charge of the water detail. We now heat water in a pan placed on top of the stove during the morning so that we can wash our hands before lunch. John Henry with Daniel's help checks on the toilet tissue supply for the boys; Gladys with Emma does the same for the girls' toilet.

During these wonderful crisp days, even I've joined in playing outside. A favorite game is "Chance." It is marvelous the joy and sheer exuberance derived from so simple an activity. All the children, except one, are on the steps. The one who is "It" stands in front and then they, all but one, flee around to the back corners of the schoolhouse. Giving them a little time, "It" calls out, "I'm coming!" No one knows which direction he will appear. Once he has touched anyone with his soft rubber ball, that individual must join him in capturing all the others. It is a frenzied, exciting game with all running here and there trying to return to home base, the steps, without being caught. Time after time, they run out. When I play, of course, I am the "big catch."

It was after one of those frantic noontime periods when everyone tumbled into their seats breathless and joyfully tired. Suddenly I realized Chris was not in his. Did anyone know whether he had to go home for some reason, I queried.

"Nope. He's lying out on the steps," offered Aaron.

Strange for Chris to act like this–he was not one who usually caused any trouble but I thought "boys will be boys."

Once outside, I saw him fully stretched out on the wide lower step.

"Chris, this is no way to behave. You are too big a boy to set a bad example for the little ones. Now, you get up."

His face was flushed and he was perspiring profusely which I attributed to all the physical activity in which we had recently participated.

"Can't, Miss Todd." He looked at me and gave me a lop-sided grin.

"Christian Yoder, what do you mean–you can't–or you won't?"

"Can't, Miss Todd, " and he began to open up his pants and from within I saw a huge bulge in the abdominal wall of protruding flesh.

I felt the color drain from my own face. "Don't move, Chris. We'll get you taken care of–just don't move," and I screamed, "Dorothy!"

Quickly the Amish girl was at my side. "Listen to me carefully, Dorothy. Run to Mrs. Bontrager's and tell her to telephone Mrs. Martin to come to the school at once–there is an emergency. We have to take Chris to the doctor in Wakarusa. Then tell her to call up Dr. Bower to say Mrs. Martin and I are bringing Christian up–he has a huge hernia. Then tell her to contact Chris' father in some way and explain all that has happened. Do you have all that?"

Radiant with purpose, she almost clicked to attention and nodded "yes."

"Come right back. I need you here."

Chris, still lying down, worked the bulge back within the abdominal cavity. "This has happened before, but not so bad."

This latest development gave me some relief, "Do you think you can walk to the car?"

"Oh, sure, Miss Todd. The worst is over now."

Mrs. Martin arrived within fifteen minutes. From the black felt hat perched squarely on her head to the black kid-gloved hands gripping the steering wheel, she was going to be thoroughly in command of the situation.

"Christian, can you get into the back seat of the car?"

"Yes, Mrs. Martin."

Slowly Dorothy and I helped him mount the high running board. Mrs. Martin had a pillow and blanket prepared.

"Get yourself as comfortable as possible–and we'll be off."

I only had time to tell Dorothy that she and Grace were in charge until I returned.

Idle chatter was immediately discouraged, "Driving takes up all my concentration."

High in the air, Mrs. M.'s Model T was immaculate–she made Dorothy clean Chris' shoes before he got in–but vintage. We jolted along at a breathtaking thirty-five miles per hour; the route until we reached Southwest was absolutely tortuous. From Southwest to Morningstar there was improvement, fewer pot-holes and ruts in the graveled surface, from there on into Wakarusa the road was almost good.

Portly and genteel Dr. Bower was waiting for us, "You must have broken all the speed laws, Rebecca. Now, you two sit here while I take Christian inside with me–this isn't for ladies to see."

We had waited perhaps fifteen minutes in weighty silence–I remembered my mother telling me how a favorite cousin had died of a stangulated hernia because it was not attended to–what Mrs. Martin was mentally experiencing I had no idea. Her face was rigid without a trace of expression.

A big man burst in. His bronzed face twisted in anxiety, "Where's my boy?"

"He's with the doctor. Calm yourself, man. He'll be all right."

"Thanks. Right neighborly–all you've done, Rebecca." He tipped his hat to me.

"Second Commandment, Jacob."

Chris' father knocked on the examining room door and hearing a response, entered.

A short time later Dr. Bower came out, "Nice diagnosis, young lady–you may have saved his life. Now, you ladies can go home. We can take care of everything from here on in."

Climbing up into the car, Mrs. Martin proved as intent on her driving as before, so I said nothing until we left town. I wished to discuss her grandson with her.

"James Buchanan," I had decided it more advantageous to use his full name, "is a remarkably talented young boy."

No response.

"He is without a doubt the most exceptional child in the entire school."

Still no response.

"A brilliant boy with the possibility of a spectacular future. I hope you are giving some thoughts to his higher education and his future."

Instinctively I knew I had gone too far with this last remark, but a response I did get.

"Young woman, there is no one in this world who is more fully aware of James' capabilities and talents than myself. To predict one's future is impossible–but, there are many fine words other than the Holy Scriptures. In the words of Socrates, 'There is only one good, knowledge, and one evil, ignorance.' Above all things I want James to be a good man."

The subject was closed. During the last mile it was impossible to say anything anyway as the road was far too rutty. I arrived at the school rather disheveled physically and mentally, but I left Mrs. Martin with the impression I would like to know this stalwart lady better.

Entering the schoolroom I was greeted with clamorous singing. Grace was in front of the school energetically conducting a round; three different groups were belting out, "Row, Row, Row Your Boat Gently Down the Stream." Dorothy sat in my desk chair calmly surveying all. As she put it, "I was maintaining order–should there be a need."

The end of another unforgettable day! When I thought over all the events of the past hours, I could not quite believe what I had done myself–from somewhere, within or from above, I had been given an unaccountable strength and guidance with which to prevail over my inexperience and lack of knowledge.

—◆—

Although a severe winter had been predicted, we were still to experience a lasting snow. The days were cold but not unbearably so, with temperatures in the mid-twenties. Inside everyone seemed contented working on their own particular interest. The seventh and eighth grades were both studying Longfellow pieces from their *Elison Readers*. The seventh with "Evangeline" and the eighth, "The Courtship of Miles Standish." Both favorites of the entire school, but the love story of Patricia Mullins and John Alden was without a doubt the chosen one.

Quite unexpectedly one day, our tranquillity was shattered by a pounding on the front door. It was the photographer who had arrived without notice to take the school's annual picture. The children seemed to me to be in a particularly shabby condition on this day. The picture had to be taken–it was now or never–for the photographer was far too busy a man to return at a scheduled time.

It was miserably cold day outside and the man himself was of an unpleasant nature.

"Hurry up! I haven't got all day."

Dorothy and Grace were assigned to spruce up the two first grades while I consulted with Daniel. I knew the Amish did not like to have their pictures taken for religious reasons but I hoped to appeal to his school spirit of camraderie.

"Miss Todd, you know it is written 'Ye shall not make for yourself a graven image...' "

"Yes, I do, Daniel–but for the sake of Froggy Bottom and posterity, it would be wonderful to have all the children included in the picture. The Amish children if they so wish could turn their faces away from the camera; they do not need to take a photograph for remembrance but it would be so nice for the other pupils to have one with all their classmates."

Daniel seemed most appreciative of my solution. I had found a reasonable way out for him.

Finally we had everyone huddled in three rows from little to big on the east side of the steps–the wind was less forceful there but still the teeth were chattering and the bodies shivering.

I looked at Orval and told him to use his handkerchief.

"Ain't got one–only my sleeve." With which he proceeded to make a big and effective sweep across his face. "That better?"

Norman's coat was closed with a horse blanket safety pin; Emma's high topped shoes were both unlaced; Susie's one braid was untied; Vilma had my work sweater over her thin coat; Charlie's stocking cap had started to unravel–but all, including each and everyone of my Amish children, looked directly into the camera and not one smiled. What a picture this one will be!

—◆—

Thursday, the last Thursday in the month, is Thanksgiving and a legal holiday. By Wednesday everyone's spirits were extra high, mine included. A light snow had been falling for the past two days with a big drop in the temperature. All the children were "praying" to have sledding and skating weather for Thursday.

Mrs. B. is going to have a big family dinner with some twenty Bontragers sitting down to eat. She had been cleaning for days as would my own mother. Thanksgiving in Indiana is almost as festive a holiday as Christmas. The basic menus are the same in town and country–turkey, candied yams, stuffing, pumpkin and mincemeat pies.

One dish served in the country which is not found on town people's table is their famed rich and succulent dried sweet corn. Mrs. B. on a special occasion had served it to me. Even in the country, it is a treat as so much work goes into its preparation.

As Mrs. B. explained the dried corn, the milk corn of the field variety, is first cut off the cob, then dried on a drier or by the sun which is a most laborious task. After being dried, it is stored in tightly sealed glass containers until needed. The night before it is to be served, it is soaked in water so it can reabsorb fluid. After the corn is drained, it is mixed with brown sugar and cream.

Knowing how much I savored her sweet corn Mrs. B., as busy as she has been during these past days, found time to prepare a big dish for the entire Todd family.

When I tried to thank her she said, "Isn't that what Thanksgiving is supposed to mean–sharing?"

In the schoolroom on late Wednesday afternoon everything seemed to take on a slightly chaotic air–and I let it be so. My three third graders were reciting together in very loud whispers–Heaven, only knows why, "Over the river and through the woods to Grandmother's house we go."

I overhead Omar and Aaron in a deep confab and didn't interrupt but thought strange are the ways of education when Aaron distinctly said, "Speak for yourself, John."

The Holiday was here!

— ◆ —

Like all good things the happy day, Thanksgiving, with friends and family passed all too soon. My dad let me drive his new Ford back on Thursday night. I was supposed to return it on Saturday after picking up my monthly check at the Trustee's.

Honestly I am beginning to think I am my father's favorite–maybe it is because he didn't have any boy near my age group among his children. I sort of substituted as one and when I was younger he shared so much with me. No doubt I was always considered a "tom-boy" in our village. Certainly it was a great privilege to be allowed to drive his new car. What I have not mentioned is that I have been taking home-styled driving lessons from Jennie's beau since mid-October.

Late Thursday afternoon I returned while it was still light, so it was quite early as the days have become much shorter. I was driving very carefully and slowly; there was a light cover of snow on the road. Everything had gone very well until I turned the last corner before Bontrager's house. I must have taken it too wide for the right side just slipped off and Dad's Model T stopped against a boulder at the ditch's edge. I climbed out trembling.

Thank Heaven many of Mrs. B.'s dinner guests were still there–the men walked down in a group to survey the damage and lifted the car up and set it straight on the road.

Eli was there and was most matter-of-fact about my crisis. "No great problem–those little bumps and lost paint Joe Pletcher can fix up tomorrow while you're in school–your pa will never know the difference."

Joe Pletcher had the garage at Southwest and Eli had him come up early Friday morning. As predicted he said we would have the car back by the afternoon, "Henry Ford made it real easy when he said, 'you can have any color car you want as long as it's black'–the paint job will be the easiest."

Although I was still very worried about the car, I did not have much time to think about it as everyone seemed re-energized with their own holiday. At the first recess my desk was surrounded by Dorothy, Grace, Mary, James and Bobby. James was the spokesman.

"Miss Todd, we must seriously begin to think of our Christmas program. We do not know if you are aware, but it is the custom here at Froggy Bottom that everyone participates in this program. Each child either sings or recites a poem. Usually they have all been given their assignments by this time. As you know some are not as speedy as others. All parents and friends are invited–it is a big event!"

"Actually I have not been as negligent as you children may think. Over Thanksgiving I gave the Christmas program much thought–and I came up with what I consider an original idea for Froggy Bottom. How would you like to present a play?"

First a shock wave rippled through the group, quickly followed by beaming faces and questioning eyes.

"Who would write the play?" queried James.

"I had thought of an adaptation–like Charles Dicken's "Christmas Carol."

"How could we give a play here? We have no stage," commented practical Mary.

James with one fell swoop shot down all opposition. "A wire can be stretched across the room, sheets can be used for curtains–we can move Miss Todd's desk out from where it sits–that protrusion can be used as center stage."

At this point with enthusiasm high, I suggested all work on individual outlines and proposals, and we would have a committee meeting at noon to finalize the Christmas program project.

The rest of the morning whispers became uncontrollable. I realized I was as guilty as anyone for this disturbance, so I closed my ears to their wild chatter.

As would be expected James was readily chosen director as well as writer-adaptor; Gladys and Mary were to be his assistants. Bobby would be in charge of construction, selecting other boys to help as he needed.

With these basics down I said, "We should also be thinking of assigning the roles very soon–but then, perhaps, we should wait for James to finish his adaptation."

James blushed ever so slightly, "Miss Todd, I...rather in anticipation...I have already made a suggested list of individuals for the parts if you would like to see it."

He handed me an untidy, but legible sheet of hand-printed names. I glanced at it and said, "These are James' suggestions."

Mrs. Cratchit . . . . Mary
Bob Cratchit . . . . Charles

Tiny Tim	Norman
Marley	Chris
Scrooge	Bobby
Christmas Past	Vilma
Christmas Present	Gladys
Christmas Future	Omar

There was a unanimous acceptance of his proposed names, as I had been certain there would be.

"This is all very well–but we still have quite a few pupils who have nothing to do for this event," was no-nonsense Mary's comment.

Again there were several obvious selections. Daniel and Dorothy, due to age and religion would be in charge of the actual Program. Daniel would open and close the event with a blessing and a prayer. Because Daniel's handwriting was so beautiful he could script the text, while Abner did the art work. Dorothy would see (with her selected troop) that the programs' folders were made. Grace, of course, would be in charge of the musical events.

"We have to have group singing at least two times," inserted Mary. "Maybe 'Silent Night'..."

"Why not let Grace do her own choosing on that," broke in James.

"The third graders told me they want to sing 'Pop Goes the Weasel' 'cause they got a special sound effect," said Dorothy.

"Not very Christmas-y," commented Bobby.

Everyone nodded in agreement. Still they all decided that the three little ones should be allowed to sing their song of choice.

"Still leaves a lot not accounted for–and the play will take up quite some time," asserted James.

"There is a poem by Longfellow called "Christmas Bells" with seven stanzas each ending with the refrain... 'Peace on earth, good will to men.' If you children think it's a good idea," I said, "we could have a seven member group stand in a row before the audience–as each one finishes his recitation, he or she fades off the stage."

"Brilliant. I like that fade-off bit." James was bubbling. "Who do you have on your list, Miss Todd?"

"Dorothy, Abner, Aaron, Alma, Orval, Sadie, and with little Susie standing alone to close the poem."

James' impatience could not be bridled, "According to my list, we still have two first-graders and two second graders to place. Grace, you should be able to come up with something for this."

"What about 'Jingle Bells'? Each child can give a tinkle with sleigh bells on cue."

"Great!" was the consensus and so Amos, Katie, Emma and John Henry were also included. November ended on a surging billow of pre-nativity activities–Froggy Bottom and its students had become electrified with enthusiasm!

DECEMBER

Winter is here–the snows are deep, the temperatures low. Daily Mrs. Martin collects all the children to the west and south of school.

"I don't have my calves out in this weather–why should young children be?"

Morning and afternoon, she shuttles a regular bus line. All Froggy Bottom's pupils in this area are somehow crammed in layers in her Model T. As with most everything else with which Mrs. M. is involved, she is in complete charge. Dorothy told me the reason that they were late this morning was because Mrs. Martin had stopped dead center in the road when she overheard little Emma who was sitting on Abner's lap say, "The Yoder kids..."

She brought the Model T to a jolting halt and turned around full face.

"Young lady, do you know kids are the young of goats?"

Poor Emma, who hardly ever ventures to speak must have been made mute by this thundering semblance of woman.

"The young of Man are called children. Do you understand?"

"With that, she turned to continue en route," all this Dorothy was describing in minute detail.

The Model T under the Amish girl's narration took on human-like qualities, "Bein' hot and tired that old motor proved just as stubborn and contrary as Mrs. Martin.

"Mrs. Martin does not give up easy and must have weighted her words as bein' a bit strong with Emma 'cause she turned again and said, 'Of course, such language is not the fault of this child—she has learned such usage from her elders.'"

Dorothy mimicked Mrs. Martin's clipped nasal twang to perfection, "Abner get out and give this vehicle a hardy crank.

"In a sudden roar and sputter, we were about to take off when she added, 'I never want to hear the word, kids, used in my presence except in reference to baby goats!'

"There really ain't nothing like Mrs. Martin—God certainly made only one."

I looked at this delightful girl-woman and remembered her words of the other day, "I dress Amish, but I think different inside." I wondered then where her path in the world would take her.

—♦—

Two days later, Abner did not arrive with the rest of Mrs. Martin's brood. Omar, his brother, reported that he was not ill and rather off-handedly remarked, "The steers gotta be fed—the horse tank froze thick. It was his turn today."

On this particular day the wind was cruelly fierce—whipping snow in swirls of crystallized icy slivers. When Abner did appear he looked as if he had been frost-covered in white from stocking cap to boot tops. His outright stiff eyebrows and frozen tears lended a bizarre aspect to his blotchy red and purple face.

"Miss Todd, I think I froze my fingers." He lifted up his gloveless hands for me to examine his swollen red and white fingers. Before I could give any kind of verdict, Dorothy was at my side.

"Good case of frostbite I'd say." She automatically took the boy's coat off and began slowly, gently to massage the palms of his hands working up to the base of the fingers.

"Rub near—never on the fingers—gets the blood goin'— maybe we should fix a hot drink for Abner."

"Jist had to take hay to those critters of pa's. Ever since he bought them last September, they ain't been nothing but trouble."

Mary wanted to put Abner's fingers in snow water, but Dorothy overruled her. "That's the old-fashioned way—it's better to 'stimulate the circulation' says so in the *Farmer's Almanac*. And never use any salves."

—◆—

Never once did any of the children ever think of staying home during these snowy wintry days. They were overjoyed with the weather. There was little that they were called upon to do at home, and the skating and sledding were excellent. Lunch was quite literally eaten on the run by all the boys. Sledding was the sport of these days as the snow was thick.

The boys were not too keen to have the girls on the hill as Norma Jean had nearly caused a terrible accident. According to a garbled report from a defending Clara Sue and a fuming Aaron, the following is my understanding of the incident.

"Her pa told her that she could only go halfway on the hill for it was too dangerous—the hill is too big."

"Idiot woman! He meant she was only to go halfway up—not to go all the way up and get off halfway down and then start off again. There are rules for sledding. She never said nothing to nobody. Could have killed us all. Stupid female."

Not mentioned before, but another favorite pastime of the boys is "treasure-hunting" in the local dump which is in fact an old abandoned and overgrown gravel pit. Not that the country people use it, they do not; most everything they own can be found to serve a purpose, sooner or later. The townspeople of Wakarusa, however, do discard their old rubbish here.

The scavengers jealously guard and boast of their "finds." Sometime in November before the snows came Bobby and Charlie had been doing a routine Saturday afternoon search in the dump when they came upon a rectangular enamel metal table top. Immediately they saw it as the answer to their prayers—they would have the fastest sled in Froggy Bottom.

Secretly they brought it to school, housing it unknown to me in the wood shed. Whispers were many but I was unsuspecting. Certainly I realized Bobby and Charlie had achieved a certain unprecedented prestige among the male segment of the school.

All this background information, I was to learn after the fact from Dorothy.

On this particular day when the snow, wind and temperature factors all met the boys' critical criterion, the "Big Push" was to be given. Of course, Bobby and Charlie were to be the pilots.

Within a few minutes after all the boys raced to the top of the hill, the launch and disaster struck. The table top took off like a shooting star and rather than follow the regular downhill route it careened bullet-like off to the left streaking straight for the tree-filled ravine. A crashing thump brought it still carrying its two passengers to a dead stop. The white snow was spattered red with blood. Charlie was sprawled out to the left of the badly scarred poplar tree. Bobby was sitting upright, looking absolutely dazed, in a snowbank with blood running down his face.

This account was given to me by James, who was deeply bemoaning the fate of his classmates and the future of "his" play–both Charlie and Bobby had major roles in the Christmas play production.

John Henry and Amos had run ahead to alert me of the accident. After my experience in the fall with the poison sumac, I had been wise enough to completely resupply and add to the First Aid cabinet. More water was put on the stove to heat.

A contingent of shamefaced boys arrived, the able bodies supporting the two lame, bloodied and bruised victims. All were guilt-ridden; all had been involved in this secret and dangerous expedition which had gone so wrong.

John Henry was the only one among the boys willing to talk, "James told them not to do it–they had no steerer."

After the initial clean-up was made, swabbing and cleansing gravel, bark-filled wounds, removing clotted blood and cutting away matted hair, the picture was less grim. The boys were badly mangled and lacerated but otherwise they apparently had no broken bones. Charlie was definitely the most battered-looking of the two. A plum-sized, colored mass had begun to protrude above his left eye, his upper lip had thickened to reach his nostrils and there was a large hairless patch on his head revealing a nasty gaping hole.

"Miss Todd," he begged, speaking with great difficulty, "please don't send us home now. What's Mamma going to say when she sees me?"

Anna Mae, his little third grade sister tried to be solicitous, "Charlie, don't worry–don't you remember how you said when it was so hot last summer you wanted a haircut like Uncle Hank's?" (Henry Weaver was the very bald grocer-meatcutter in Foraker.)

No one thought of sending them to the doctor and because both boys were so persistent that they did not want to go home, I relented. However, I still was not certain about Bobby's nose; the bone might be cracked even though the bleeding had stopped. His most painful injury was a badly bruised and wrenched right knee. He was stoically silent, apparently feeling he was being justly punished for his sins.

Only James was now verbalizing, "Scrooge can walk with a cane but how can kindly Bob Cratchit look like a one-eyed Cyclops, an ogre–this is just terrible!"

"James, don't you ever think of anyone but yourself?" It was a stern Mary lecturing, "YOU and this play–that's all you can think about–it's nearly two weeks yet–flour paste can cover up lots."

Everyone knew that a punishment had to be meted out. The boys of Froggy Bottom had disobeyed the rules. They patiently awaited my announcement. Although I had been relatively lenient up to this point, I also knew I had to make my position clear.

"Today we have had an unfortunate accident which never should have occurred–because the boys of Froggy Bottom disobeyed school rules there will be a complete and total suspension of all activities on the Hill and Pond for the next two weeks. Play time will be allowed only on the school grounds."

Not one voice of protest was heard. Silence. Then Alma said, "Remember Lot's wife." As if this said it all. Obedience and respect are expected to be cardinal virtues at Froggy Bottom.

If the children did not object, someone must have decided the penalty I inflicted was too severe. Days of heavy sleet and icy rain followed. There could have been no sledding nor skating in any event.

— ♦ —

Christmas time and the school's big program were rapidly approaching. Every noon was devoted to rehearsals. James took the east and Grace the west side of the schoolroom. Without much help on my part, James had brilliantly adapted Dicken's "Christmas Carol" to Froggy Bottom. This would be the first play ever presented here–no one could have taken their responsibility more seriously than James. He was a born perfectionist.

"Slave-driver!" Vilma poutingly called him as she repeated her Christmas Past lines for the umpteenth time.

Grace on the other side of the room grouped her members of the three lower grades together. Her "Jingle Bells" selection is turning into a production nightmare–the four first and second graders can sing the song well enough, but try as Grace will, she can not get John Henry and Amos to ring their sleigh bells on cue. The third graders pose no difficulty, but day-after-day Grace and the collected audience must endure listening to "Pop Goes the Weasel" so Clara Sue can once again demonstrate Froggy Bottom's loudest mouth-cheek pop.

My seven are relegated to the front of the room where daily we work on their individual stanzas and exits. Susie's big smile and closing curtsy and backward leave are so original that I have no intention of changing anything–they are bona fide show-stoppers.

Perhaps my own conscience was a bit disturbed. Skating is now possible, but I have not given in. Rather I began reading *Hans Brinker–The Silver Skates* which the children have dearly loved from page one. The reading sessions have become more frequent and longer. Mary Dodge's words have captivated all at Froggy Bottom.

During one of those torpid, wintry days James approached my desk evidently very perturbed. "Miss Todd, what are we doing about putting up our theater curtains? I do not want to wait until the last minute to see if everything works or not."

There are times for levity but this definitely was not one of them; the child was so earnest about "his" play. "Calm yourself, James. I have arranged everything but the curtains. My brother is coming on Friday to help Bobby; he is bringing heavy construction wire, ladders and whatever he might need to put the wire across the room. As for the curtains, I will ask the children today if their mothers would loan us some sheets."

"No. I'll take care of the curtains. I don't want them all different kinds."

Friday came with some unexpected variations. If I have not said it before my brother, Ralph, is a most kindhearted lad, generous to a fault and also an incurable dreamer. He and Horace, a boyfriend of mine whom my sister Jennie is ardently promoting and pushing in my direction as he is the only one in our crowd to have a car, were to bring a Christmas tree for my schoolroom and all the necessary items to put up the wire for the curtains.

Around two o'clock, there was a knock on the schoolroom's front door. I told Omar to open it–I was in the midst of a class and I was certain it would be Ralph and Horace.

Omar returned on the run with boggled eyes. "Its a starving Santa Claus," he finally stammered out.

"What do you mean?"

"Look!"

A more apt description might have been an "Ichabod Crane" in a red Santa Claus suit–tall, gangling and skinny–a bare two inches of hairy flesh stuck out above his four-buckle rubber boots and a bedraggled whitish beard covered his face. The children were absolutely speechless.

"Santa Claus, what an unexpected surprise. What can we do for you?"

"The Christmas season is near at hand..." Santa's voice broke in a slight adolescent squeak. "I have been working very hard this year..."

"So that's why you are so thin?"

"Yes. Actually Froggy Bottom was chosen as a stopping place today because you have some very exceptional children." Another squeak. "I'm already late–so I'd like to use your desk chair, Miss Todd."

John Henry hoarsely asked, "How'd he know her name?"

Susie adamantly responded, "Santa Claus knows everything."

The chair was quickly placed on the east side of the room between the two windows. Santa Claus majestically sat down, his skinny legs wide apart and his back tall and straight. The children lined up. One by one they passed to tell Santa Claus what they wanted for Christmas.

When it was Norman's turn, he refused to go, "Santa Claus ain't for the likes of us."

When the others were finished, Santa Claus himself squatted down by Norman's morose little figure and cajoled him into saying, "A pair of skates like Hans."

Exit one Santa Claus, and enter Brother Ralph and friend Horace. Some of the older children gave each other suspicious looks, sizing my brother up and down, but not one of the smaller ones truly questioned.

Only John Henry in full innocence went over, stooped and carefully looked at Ralph's boots, "Just like Santa Claus."

"My brother has the same kind, too," was Emma's comment.

The Christmas tree, a truly beautiful bushy specimen is centered where Santa's chair had been, between the two windows to the east. Ralph and Horace had cut it out of the woods belonging to Horace's uncle. I am quite certain he knows nothing about this, so I did not ask any questions. I promised my family I would bring the tree back to our home when school let out for the Christmas holidays.

Anna Mae came up to me and asked, "Is it time?"

I must have looked rather blank as Norma Jean chirped, "Can I ask Daniel for his hat?"

Then I knew. It had been decided we were to draw names for Christmas—the names on the slips had long since been written and folded in three—this was another new experience for Froggy Bottom's children and they were all very excited about it.

Daniel good-naturedly allowed his hat to be used although I am not certain if he approved of the purpose for which it served.

As the three third graders were passing the hat around I had a momentary chance to speak to Ralph. "Where did you come up with that outfit and idea?"

"The Kiwanis–I do janitor work there–I borrowed it–Froggy Bottom is considered a good cause."

While the boys were helping put up the wire for the curtains and this project took in everyone of Froggy Bottom's male members, mostly in an advisory capacity, the girls were gracefully draping the tree with multi-colored paper chains made during the past weeks.

As I said good-bye for the weekend, I reminded the children, "Remember, next week everyone is to make his own ornament for the Christmas tree–a prize will be given to the one considered the most original at the Christmas Day Program."

—◆—

Monday morning, Mrs. Martin arrived as usual with her load of children. Normally she drove off in a jerky lurch; today she alighted carrying in a huge closed cardboard box on her extended arms.

"These are sheets that can be used as curtains for the play James is directing." Her tone suggested that his would be no less than a New York theatrical production. Without another word she left.

As I opened the sealed carton, an aromatic whiff of lavender scented the room. Inside were stacks of beautiful hand-embroidered, carefully ironed and folded sheets, heavily creased and yellowed with time.

Dorothy, who is always quick with an observation, looked around first to see that we were alone then remarked, "I guess these musta' come from Baby's Hope Chest."

Alma and Katie were absent this Monday. I casually asked if everything were alright in the Yoder home to which Orval retorted, "Depends on how you view things. Tomorrow all of us Amish won't be here. There's a big wedding at the Yoder's—Sarah is marryin' up with Aaron Zimmerman's son, Noah."

To verify Orval's report I looked in Dorothy's direction, who only too gladly added her affirmative commentary.

"That's right. Most of our weddings happen during November and December when there ain't such pressin' work—I suppose that also why Tuesday and Thursdays are chosen 'cause these are the lightest days of the week. Our weddings bear no kin to English ones."

A nervous quiver was running through the schoolroom. The children themselves set a racing pace to recitation. They were all looking forward to making their tree ornaments. During the weekend I had gone scavenger hunting myself—Mr. K. of Kline's had again been my benefactor. I had a box of ribbon scraps. From somewhere Brother Ralph had secured small cans of different colored paint, glue and tacks. I suppose the "donor" was the Kiwanis Club but due to Ralph's past history and the rather mischievous glint in his eyes when he presented them to me, I felt it better not to delve too deeply into the matter.

The lower grades were well into "their" project by mid-morning. John Henry was modeling an angel which he intended to paint. Emma was making "a horse with long ears." Susie was pasting carefully selected bits of cloth onto a small box. It was Norman's work which truly caught my eye. He was patiently sticking cloves into a hedge apple.

"An orange or regular apple might have been better but we don't have none—this apple didn't cost nothing. Miss Todd, could you please save me some red ribbon so I kin tie it on the tree?"

— ♦ —

Whispering is always the big disciplinary problem, as I have often mentioned, but this morning it came from an unexpected source. Daniel who normally is the model student was caught frequently leaning over to Dorothy's desk. They were both so involved that my famous black look never penetrated their conversational milieu. I finally had to say, "Daniel, don't you think your talk with Dorothy can wait until lunch time?" He blushed crimson and sat rigid and mute until noon.

As I dismissed the classes for lunch, Dorothy came quickly to my desk.

"It weren't Daniel's fault–I was asking him about our weddings."

Rather shamed-faced I said, "Wash your hands and eat lunch, Dorothy. After, I'd like very much to hear about Amish weddings."

Fifteen minutes later, Dorothy with notes in hand began without preamble, "Courtin' is very secret–nobody ever knows quite for certain 'cause the boy, the young buck as they say, goes to the girl's house after the old folks go to bed–but, there are signs. This past summer when Aaron bought another farm, people began talkin' that Noah might be gettin' hitched–but we weren't sure who the girl would be until when it was announced at church service some Sundays ago."

"Does a girl have a dowry?"

"Every Amish girl always has quilts and coverlets that have been made for her during the years. Some have more than others. Sarah Yoder and Noah Zimmerman will make a good match. She has a chest full of towels, blankets and quilts that her ma made for her. Eli, her pa, is a fine carpenter and has made some chairs, tables and beds for her–

besides he is giving them a fine Guernsey cow. They'll do all right."

"What clothes do the bride and groom wear for the wedding?"

"Nothing extra-special– everything for the bride and groom is new and handmade–but, for both of them, they dress like on Sunday."

"What is the religious ceremony like?"

"This part is usually long-winded maybe takin' some three hours–this year the religious service will be held at Harvey Ramer's house about a mile away from the Yoder's. I think the service is unusually long so that the cookin' couples can get everything ready. The cooks, never close relatives, but both men and women, couples, arrive at daylight at the home of the bride. The wedding meal and its celebration is a big part of the day. Lots of chickens, roast duck, cakes, pies–tables full of good country cooking. Oh, I almost forgot, it's the custom for the bridegroom to cut off all the heads of the fowls–I don't know the reason for this, neither does Daniel. Trestle tables are set up throughout the house–this wedding is goin' be a big one. I heard that Noah even telephoned to relatives in Pennseevanie– they're comin' by train."

"Who is invited to the wedding?"

"Relatives mostly–but then everyone here one way or another is a relative. Ain't no invitations like you folks– jist word of mouth by the groom goin' around and asking people to come."

"Each wedding guest is expected to bring a gift–my grandma is taking a kerosene lamp that she had during her good days in Middlebury. Most gifts are for the house or small farms tools that Noah can use in the barn or shed–in all things we are practical people."

"Are there any decorations in the house?"

"You mean flowers or such. No, but there is lots of extra good baking done."

"How long does it last?"

"All day and into the night for the young people–it's one day of eatin' and then in the late afternoon the singin' begins–lots have to go home and do chores. Some of the young people stay on if it was previously arranged or come back. There's lots of singing and as the older folks leave, the songs become less and less religious."

"Don't they do anything else but eat and sing?"

"We here in this community are still awfully conservative–the people in Pennseevanie, they're the rich ones–they've become more worldly with their weddings. Some of their young people even play barn games–like 'Skip To My Lou' but our Bishops say that is a road which leads to damnation."

Dorothy's closing comment, "I suppose you could say an Amish wedding is most serious–everyone present knows that the couple now begins their responsibilities for all of their life–a wedding, a marriage is till death."

— ♦ —

Our school's program and the Christmas holidays were still over a week away but already everyone was bustling with nervous energy. Gifts had begun to appear beneath the tree–they were wrapped in a variety of original ways–in the weekly *Prairie Farmer* and binder twine, a heavy brown paper sack, a piece of burlap cut from a fertilizer bag and tied with dark blue rick-rack taping, unbleached muslin and green yarn.

Grace as usual acted as representative for the older girls grouped around my desk. They realized I was "new on teachin' " so they came to offer their advice.

"Us girls got together," began the seventh grader, "and we figured it's already too late for you to get the treats made."

Probably I gave them one of my well-known blank looks.

Grace continued, "At Christmas here in Froggy Bottom, it is normal to serve some refreshments to the parents."

I smiled weakly for Mrs. B. had not forewarned me of this.

"So it has been decided among us–that is, if you don't mind–that Mary will bake drop cookies, Gladys and I 'cause we live close kin make up fudge this weekend. Dorothy will bring some of Grandma Mast's sugar cookies. Do you like our idea?"

Again, I smiled and nodded positively.

Grace went on, "That should be enough if you get Mrs. Bontrager to help you with the utensils and the cider."

This past weekend I bought a duplicator in Goshen's News Bookstore. Perhaps, this is too fancy a name, but it does make copies. It is a shallow rectangular pan which is filled with gelatin. One makes the master copy on specially inked hectograph paper and presses it face down upon the absorbing jelly. The children are intrigued–they have never seen anything like this before.

Daniel who has such beautiful handwriting and is able to script write is to prepare our Christmas program. I brought him some of Ralph's special drawing nibs. Of course, Abner is to design all the artistic layout. The front piece is an exact replica of Froggy Bottom School centered in a huge Christmas wreath. He had Daniel write in Old English script "Merry Christmas to One and All." I also detect James' fine fingerprints here. At the bottom in smaller-sized script is to be written December 20, 1922.

The inside of the to-be folder is the actual program–it fills the entire page (a copy of which I am attaching here). Another master copy has to be made for this sheet, too.

CHRISTMAS PROGRAM
Froggy Bottom School

Greeting .... Miss Helen Todd
Blessing .... Daniel Troyer
Group Singing, "O, Little Town of Bethlehem"
.... led by Grace Hunsberger
"Jingle Bells." .... Amos Miller, Katie Yoder, Emma Stutzman, John Henry Bender

The Play "Christmas Carol"
by Charles Dickens .... Adapted and directed by James Buchanan Martin

CAST

Mrs. Bob Cratchit .... Mary Michael
Bob Cratchit .... Charles Weaver
Tiny Tim .... Norman Knox
Marley .... Christian Yoder
Christmas Past .... Vilma Knox
Christmas Present .... Gladys Rohrer
Christmas Future .... Omar Hostetler

Scrooge.. Robert Hartman
"Pop Goes the Weasel"......................... Anna Mae Weaver,
Norma Jean Herr,
Clara Sue Good

"Christmas Bells"
by Henry W. Longfellow.................. Dorothy Mast, Abner
Hostetler, Aaron Michael,
Alma Yoder, Orval Miller,
Sadie Smucker, Susie Cripe

Group Singing "Silent Night"... led by Grace Hunsberger

Benediction .... Daniel Troyer

Gift-giving and refreshments to follow program.

The entire school was involved in making the programs. Mrs. B. some months ago had given me a dilapidated table. Eli brought it down in his spring wagon, strengthened its legs and I painted it a vivid yellow. This is where I set up our production of the Christmas programs.

Daniel and Abner's master copies looked excellent, clear and beautifully designed. Mary as the most meticulous of the older girls was chosen to apply the paper to the jelly; it had to be thoroughly but gently pressed from bottom to top using the sponge ruler that came with the gelatin set. Vilma was to see that all copies were acceptable. Emma and Sadie carefully tapped the papers together into neatly lined up stacks.

"Henry Ford should see our assembly line," quipped James, "but whoever has seen or heard of using purple at Christmas time?"

Of course, James' observation had merit but with this gelatin set, its special ink only comes in this violet color.

"Don't be so picky, James. Never before did we have anything and now you go and find fault with everything."

Coming from placid Vilma, this remark must have taken James slightly off-guard for he said not another word.

The front piece was all the copying we could do in one day. After making fifty good copies, I emptied the gelatin mixture; I had to make up another batch.

The second day's work was even more complicated and exacting. Mary had to be careful in applying the paper for the front piece was already in place. Vilma had to inspect for clarity and then fold the sheet exactly in two. Again Emma and Sadie put together the finished program in orderly piles.

Everything was progressing nicely, or so I thought, but not according to James. He was fussing terribly that the audience would be facing the stage (where my desk had been) off-center. Due to his overearnest persistence, Eli had already brought chairs from the Southwest Mennonite and the Yellow Creek Brethren churches. The three first grade rows, being portable, were relined along the walls.

Thursday before the last day was to be the day of dress rehearsal of the play–the schoolroom looked festive and gay draped in colored chains and decorated with green pine boughs. The Christmas tree had a charm of its own being hung with the individually made tree ornaments of the children. All but the cast were seated as the audience on this afternoon. Daniel was to open up the curtains.

"No, Daniel–not all the way. First I'll come out and give a short greeting. When I have finished and retire–then you can open them wide."

The beginning was a bit bumpy but the play and children quickly settled down. James was high in color and nervous. He had worked so hard. Scrooge was most effective with his stoop and cane. Less in character perhaps, but with all the signs of the sledding accident carefully disguised, was Charlie as Bob Cratchit who wore a moth-eaten gray wig and huge dark-rimmed glasses.

The children adored the play. Then we heard an unprofessional cry from behind the curtain.

"Where's Marley. I can't believe it–I'll have to go in his place."

The play nevertheless ended with enthusiastic applause from the children. It was still too early to dismiss school for the day, but it was also evident that the children would never concentrate on any lessons. So Grace took her singing groups to practice their songs and I told Dorothy to take her group to recite their poem.

James came up to my desk fuming, I tried to placate him saying, "Maybe Chris is ill."

"I should have known better–shirt-tail Amish that's what he is. He's no kin to our other school Yoders, but he just removed. It's sure his parents won't let him appear in a play.

"I have been like the 'Little Red Hen' through this entire production–so I'll just have to do it–I'll be Marley, too. I know all the lines."

This time I truly had difficulty in not smiling, James was taking himself so seriously. If melodrama could be personified, it would be called James!

—♦—

The last day of school finally arrived. The sun shone on the glistening white snow. It was a beautiful winter afternoon. Mrs. B. had lent me a white cloth for my yellow table. Pitchers of cider, glasses and plates of fudge and cookies were set out in readiness. The school yard was filled with cars and buggies. We had over thirty parents and friends present.

Grace and Mary helped the ladies with their coats. Aaron and Omar were on the boys' side to aid the men with their hats and coats. Susie and John Henry gave out the programs.

"Good turnout," I heard Mrs. B. say to Mrs. Bender.

"Everyone wants to see this young schoolmarm with her fancy ways."

Everything went as planned–well, almost. There were a few little exceptions. Of course John Henry and Amos did not jingle their sleigh bells on cue, but no one ever thought that they would. Bob Cratchit's wig came off at one point revealing Charlie's shaved and still bandaged head. Marley's chains got caught on the foot of a desk used on the set; Gladys' robe of "Christmas Present" opened in back giving the audience a complete view of her long-johnned figure when she turned. The famed Clara Sue "pop" would not pop, try as she might, for "Pop Goes the Weasel." Sadie Smucker had to be coached on the last line "of peace on earth, good will to men" which was the only line which had been constantly repeated. Daniel's Blessing and Benediction, as I should have known by this time, were both silent prayers.

On the whole everyone, parents and friends included, were happy. It was a season to be jolly.

As the refreshments were being enjoyed and everyone was adding their personal commentary to the program, John Henry clapped his hands shouting, "Our skinny Santa Claus is here!"

And so he was. Without ado, he began handing out the presents under the tree with the help of John H. I was the recipient of many—mine were opened and exhibited on my desk top. The children walked around proudly describing their gifts to me—applebutter, hand-embroidered pillow cases, relish, towels, cracklins.

"Mamma bought that for Miss Todd at the five and ten cent store," said a puffed-up Aaron as he pointed to an iridescent salmon-colored, flower-shaped candy dish.

At this point Alma tugged at my sleeve, "I couldn't put our Christmas gift under the tree, so I put it in your coat pocket."

There was one reaction I could not help but notice among my children at Froggy Bottom. They were more interested to know if the person whose name they had drawn liked the gift they had been given than in opening up the one they had received.

As one would imagine many of the gifts had a practical turn—I'll try to remember some of them. Grace received a cookbook, recipes collected from the Holdeman Mennonite Church. There were many homemade wooden toys evidently the handiwork of a loving father—tops, whistles, a small flute. Then there was a bag of marbles with ball and jacks which was the envy of all the boys; James gave that to Bobby, I believe. There was an embroidery hoop for Mary and Clara Sue received her longed-for crotchet hook. There were handkerchiefs, some embroidered with an initial, edged with tatting or just finely hemmed. A package of gum was given to someone and certainly considered a great luxury. Amos received a yo-yo which Brother Oval was enormously pleased to have in the family. Every child had his gift—one that was chosen especially for him.

The time had arrived for the prize to be given for the most original Christmas tree ornament. I left the judging to Santa Claus who was playing his role with all the panache of a true troubadour. He carefully picked up, turned and praised each "work of art" with just the right and most appropriate of words.

Everyone was in great suspense. For some time Santa held Norman's cloved hedge apple, turning and smelling it.

"My dear children–there is no doubt that this ornament is the most original–all has been taken from Nature and created into a Christmas beauty." Santa held it high for all to see. "The winner."

The ragged Tiny Tim of the day, Norman Knox stepped forword in unbelieving wonder. Santa Claus stooped and pulled out a beautifully gift-wrapped package from his big sack.

"This is for you, my little lad. Your Christmas tree ornament won Froggy Bottom's prize of the year!"

"Open it, Norman! Open it," was the chant that spread through the room.

Carefully he removed the glossy paper, folded it and the ribbon before taking up the shoe box. He lifted the lid and his eyes became the size of saucers. Speechless, Norman, held up a pair of clip-on skates. Ralph had carefully cleaned, polished and put new leather straps on his old skates. Tears rimmed the child's eyes.

"There really is a Santa Claus–they're jist like Hans."

Everyone was wreathed in smiles and good-byes. I told them to take their tree ornaments. Side-by-side Santa and I waved to the departing children, saying, "Merry Christmas One and All! See You Next Year."

John Henry had been halfway across the schoolyard walking hand-in-hand with his mother when he raced back. "Miss Todd, where you goin', " his eager little face and crossed eyes set in a sea of anguish, "for a whole year?"

I gave John Henry a big loving hug. He had just given me my finest, my best, Christmas present.

"Don't worry–that's just a way grown-ups have of talking sometimes. I'll be here when vacation is over. 'See you next year' just means the calendar is changing. Now run along to your mother. Merry Christmas."

Christmas was here! I was going home to be with my own family for more than two weeks. Ralph was as anxious as I to leave and get home before dark. He quickly packed the tree onto Horace's fender held secure with rope and the ever-useful binder twine. We left the closing up to Mrs. B. who thought it better to keep a fire banked during these cold days. As she is officially in charge of the upkeep of the building, I am certain she and Eli will know what to do. They both shooed me out of the school saying they would clean up everything.

After many departing hugs, I entered the cold cloakroom filled with a strange mixture of love and loneliness. Dressed in my coat and boots, I reached into my pocket for my gloves only to feel a small package. Then I remembered Alma mentioning their Christmas present had to be kept in the cold. I pulled out a neatly wrapped parcel; no doubt it contained homemade linked sausages. Then I also remembered the Yoder's had butchered last week.

How could I ever forget these past months at Froggy Bottom? Indeed, this year 1922 has been memorable and will remain an unforgettable landmark in my life.

JANUARY

The first Monday after the New Year school began once again. Everyone was present and seemed endowed with a renewed spirit of health and happiness. The children could not stop talking to each other and it took the entire first morning to get the schoolroom into an established routine once again.

The winter months are always the most relaxing in a farm community–there are farm chores but time can be found for "joshing around."

One of my first desk visitors was John Henry. He came proudly up at recess time.

"Miss Todd, I got something to tell you."

I said nothing but looked questioningly at him.

"I'm goin' be like the rest."

Still I said nothing, but certainly the look was more perplexed.

"This summer I'm goin' have my eyes operated on in Mayo Clinic."

"John Henry, that's wonderful."

Mrs. B. had once told me that the country people when they truly have serious medical problems insist upon having the very best of medical advice and treatment.

Before going for the Christmas holidays, I asked the older girls if they would like to learn how to weave. My next door neighbor in Waterford, Lucy Lockner, had promised to teach me. They would have to pay for the reeds which I would buy for them. Grace, Mary, Dorothy and Gladys all had parental approval.

Surprisingly Dorothy turns out to be the best pupil of the four; she is very adept and works with unusual diligence.

"I want to be able to recane my grandmother's favorite rocker—its seat is badly busted."

Mary's work, true to her personality, is neat and meticulous; she is making a small sewing basket. Gladys is all thumbs and has yet to know enough to make any decisions about a proposed article. Grace to my utter surprise, made many mistakes and became most irritable when I made her correct them. Come what may, it will keep them busy for the winter.

So far this week, the Hostetler boys and Chris Yoder have not attended any class.

Aaron, Omar's classmate, said with evident envy in his voice, "It's good weather for cleanin' up the woods—takin' out the dead trees and fallen limbs."

Aaron who is far from talkative wanted to say more today, but didn't know how to proceed, so I asked, "What makes it such good weather?"

"No snow, no wind. There's lots of wildlife—Chris and Abner are sure to take their rifles."

"What would they shoot?"

"Maybe panthers..."

"Aaron!"

"Well, maybe a rabbit or squirrel—they might see a fox."

On Thursday a near-blizzard began howling and all three boys were back in class. Probably to explain their absence, they brought me a piece of honeycomb oozing with thick dark liquid.

"By accident, we cut a slab off a bee tree. Miss Todd, you never tasted the like—there's nothing like wild honey—its aroma and bitter bite of deep smellin' buckwheat."

The days are cold and bright but still an unmistakable lethargy hangs over all. When the weather permits the children make huge circles in the snow and play their favorite game "Fox and Geese." On such days the furnace is lined with brightly colored wet mittens, invariably forgotten and remembered only when the scorching smell of their singeing reminds us. On those days when it is too bad even for the most hearty to play outside, the yellow table is moved aside for a wild game of "Blind's Man's Bluff." Or the seats are used for total participation in an even wilder "Change Cars for Boston." There are days I even relent and let the girls play tic-tac-toe on the blackboard. To ward off these winter doldrums I began a new book, Mark Twain's *Tom Sawyer* which proved to be one of my most brilliant choices.

One day I overheard Aaron say to his older sister, "You ain't my Aunt Polly, Mary."

But my best reward was when Orval came to me. "Miss Todd, tomorrow Amos and I gotta help with butcherin'—do you think you could hold off on Tom. We both like to know what's happenin' to them all—Tom, Jim and Huck." His small eyes pleaded.

"It's a promise—if you do that page of arithmetic before you go."

—◆—

Winter months, particularly December and January, when the outside work is less, is the time for butchering. The steers which were bought in September have been fattened and are now in prime condition. The price of beef is high so many families choose not to butcher any of their steers. Raising steers for market to increase the family income is quite new to the northern Indiana farmer's mentality. Every family however does butcher at least one or more hogs yearly depending on their size–the family and the animals.

All this background information came from an unexpected source–Mrs. B's husband Eli who is usually as communicative as a clam.

"Here our farmin' is purty simple bein' mostly alfalfa and corn and cows and pigs. The pigs follow the cows so there ain't no loss. Any corn that goes through the cow, the pig cleans up."

If I thought Eli's description of Indiana farming ways left nothing for the imagination, I found his imagery of a butchering day even more graphic.

"A rifle shot and a squeal. That's it! The men folk then pitch in–the trestle and pulleys already set-up–long practiced they hoist the dead hog–usually between 500–600 pounds–high, head down."

Eli was actually enjoying himself. He saw that I had never heard of anything like home-butchering and was very interested. Maybe he never talks because Maude is always faster than he is and never lets him finish. She had gone to her Thursday afternoon quilting session.

"The belly's slit open and the entrails pulled out–gently 'cause there ain't nothing except the squeal which don't serve so it's said here–men work fast–catching the blood– still the snow by this time has turned into red slush.

"Nearby the women has cauldrons of boiling water ready–there's much cleanin' to do–the intestines will make the casements of the sausages.

"Normally these days are raw cold–the younger women work with the men handlin' the iron kettles and cuttin' up the meat on trestled tables outside. Grinding the meat for sausages, headmeat and cracklin-making is done mainly by the older women in the summer house where they have a roaring fire in the cook stove. Cookin' and spicin' the sausage meat is done here–today, our women have it easy– all they have to do is fit the pig's gut over a machine, stuff the thing with meat, turn the handle and every so often give a twist to make a sausage link."

"From your description, I would say butchering is mostly women's work."

"Nope–that's not quite right. There's lot to be done inside and out by men and women, it's all together work. The hog got to be cut up and readied for smoking, too– hams, bacon slabs, ham hocks."

Indiana farms usually have a connecting work complex outside of the main farmhouse. Here there is a summer-house or kitchen, a woodhouse, and a smokehouse where their meats are cured. Nearby is a springhouse where the milk is placed in a deep cement tank filled with running water to keep it cool.

"Every year things get easier. Two Christmases ago I bought Maude a cracklin machine. It's a circular press which screws down, causing all the fat to leave through an outgoing channel. Before this, the men used to have to use physical force and the cracklins weren't near so brittle."

Brakes and the slamming of car doors announced Mrs. B.'s arrival.

"Cora Bender (John Henry's mother) is bringin' Maude home. Between last night's prayer meetin,' today's quilting bee and the telephone, there ain't nothing that woman don't know.

"What you two been chewing the fat about? Not waiting for an answer, Mrs. B. added, "Eli, old Lizzie Yoder's real bad–they even had Clem Iffert over."

The next day in school Alma was not present and little Katie said, "Grandma's sick."

Dorothy as always was my reliable fountain of news.

"Old Lizzie been coughin' up blood now for sometime– she's been livin' alone in *Grossdaadi Haus*, ("Grandfather's house") since Grandpa Yoder died."

"Who's Clem Iffert?"

"How'd you hear about him? A faith-healer–not that we put too much value to his doings but everybody always tries everything."

"Wasn't a real doctor called?"

"I suppose–but don't matter, Old Lizzie is goin' die. She ain't got no reason to live no more–no babies to take care of–no sewin,' no cookin.' My grandma who never says nothing about nobody did say this time, Almie's ma got high-flautin' notions not lettin' her mother-in-law do anything. It's not Amish. You gotta be needed."

—◆—

Next morning Mrs. B. called me extra early. She was fixing a special breakfast. Eli and I were going to have buckwheat pancakes. The heavy griddle had to be used for these and they were to be served with headmeat, a ground heavily-peppered mixture of hog brains.

"This will make a real woman out of you."

"Eli, spread that headmeat over Miss Todd's griddle cakes–show her how we eat them."

Although my stomach had momentarily flipped-flopped at the idea of this Indiana country culinary speciality, when I finally did taste the combination, it proved to be quite appetizing though very heavy.

"I'll have to walk to school this morning." Sometimes Eli took me in the sleigh.

"Eli, what are you goin' to do about the apple trees? Are you or aren't you going to trim them?"

"Can't rightly say, Maude. I figure it's a bit too cold."

"I don't know. They said it was going to be an extra severe winter. We ain't been snowbound once this year. It's over mid-January already."

One of my preoccupations during the closed-in days of winter were the boys. The girls were knitting, crocheting or weaving. Eli, a fine carpenter himself, as most countrymen are, suggested I let the boys make birdhouses. He became most fatherly, providing house sketches for different birds, scraps of woods, tiny nails, one small hammer and a rather defective handsaw. The boys were delighted and the gloom of January began to lighten. All worked at the now very scarred yellow table.

A problem did develop. Orval was constantly causing trouble among the other boys either by upsetting their paint on purpose or tearing up one of the other boy's birdhouse sketches. I had never seen him so unbelievably naughty. My solution was to send him home at noon with a note to his parents saying that he had been very bad and should be punished.

To my utter disbelief, Orval came back within the hour with a note for me.

"Couldn't agree with you more. Punishment is for the good of the child. That is your responsibility to do, not ours!"

Orval was the first child I ever paddled. We went to the woodshed where I turned him over my knee. This is what one calls saving face.

That same day I was to overhear a heated argument between brother and sister, Aaron and Mary, which restored my sense of humor.

"Aaron, you know it is a sin to be slothful. Now you sit down and write that composition for Miss Todd."

"I don't understand when you talk in such big words."

"Slothful–you are plain lazy!"

Then came Aaron's reply which deserves to be recorded if not for posterity in "Ripley's Believe It Or Not."

"Mary, you know well that children like I am, we inherit a sinful nature through no fault of our own..."

"Aaron, I am rapidly losing my patience. If you are smart enough to know all that, you are smart enough to write–now, write."

Aaron evidently realized his sister's tolerance had reached its limit, and his long overdue paper was presented that very day.

—◆—

Up to now, I had not found the appropriate time to discuss Clem Iffert with Mrs. B. Tonight as she darned Eli's socks, and I knit on a birthday sweater for my sister Irene, we managed to cover a wide conversational scope while sitting in front of the toasty warm kitchen range.

"Clem is a faith-healer–the word outsiders use is pow-wowing which isn't looked on with much favor as it gives these remedies an Indian flavor."

"Then there is no connection with the Indian medicine men?"

"Only in the broadest of terms in that both seek to cure. The roots of our faith-healing go back to our forefathers in Europe–in France and Germany."

"Does that mean that there are individuals who possess special healing powers?"

"Not exactly. Those who are interested in learning the art must find someone of the opposite sex to give them instructions–nothing of this is written down. These powers and their formulas have to be passed from woman to man or from man to woman."

"Will the faith-healer accept anyone for treatment?"

"I don't rightly know. They might be a bit shy of an outsider–sure that they would have to be brought by someone they, the faith-healer knows. One thing is basic, the person who is being healed has to firmly believe he is goin' to be cured or he won't be–he's gotta have blind faith."

"What about someone like old Grandmother Yoder? I understand she not conscious now."

"That don't mean much. First of all Clem went to see her–more of a courtesy call just to sorta pacify the family that they had done all that was possible. This don't usually happen. Clem normally treats in his own house–the people come to him. Nowadays there isn't much faith-healing anymore–among the older folk they still do it, but more out of habit than true belief–the young believe in a good medical doctor."

Next day Dorothy brought me the latest on Old Lizzie's condition.

"Grandma went to visit her again yesterday–the women and men, neighbors and friends, come in regular when somebody's sick. They sit around quiet like in the front room talkin' real low. Grandma said sure there won't be another visit–she's near gone."

— ♦ —

For days there had been much buzzing around. The question was when were we going to choose Froggy Bottom's representative for the township's Spelling Bee. According to all reports, it probably would be held sometime in late March or early April. Froggy Bottom had a notorious reputation of being made up of terrible spellers. Looking at the very few stars up on the "Spelling Board" I could not say that their status had improved over this year.

Everyone from the fifth grade to the eighth was allowed to participate, meaning Dorothy and Daniel along with Gladys, who can not spell "cat" without a "k," will act as referees and judges. The rules are very exacting and if not executed correctly, the contestant can be disqualified even though he has spelled the word properly.

Two teams with Grace and Mary as respective Captains were finally chosen. Grace's team was made up of James, Bobby, Omar and Abner. Mary had Vilma, Chris, Aaron and Claude. It was the consensus that Grace had the better team. The judges worked with the pupils individually and as teams at noontime on those days that were blizzardy and unfit for "man or beast" to be outside.

They began with fifth grade words and worked through to the eighth. To everyone's surprise Vilma was a very apt learner. She on occasion outspelled James, who although without a doubt was the brightest student, he had a tendency to spell phonetically.

All these days of preparation were leading up to choosing someone to represent Froggy Bottom. In order not to disappoint the others, and to put a bit of spice in our days,

I decided the last Friday in the month we would have a spell-down with the two teams. Parents and friends would be invited, and tea and cookies would be served.

— ♦ —

Geography was a favorite subject of the entire school. The subject was first taught as such in the fourth grade but there was no one who ever missed any of the sights on the maps when they were pulled down. When I came back from the Christmas holidays, I brought a rotating globe of the world. On "inside" days the children spent hours spinning and dreaming–Africa, mountains and the seas were their favorite points of interest.

On this particular morning, I was making up a geography test for my sixth graders who are particularly keen on this subject, all four of them. I was deeply engrossed wanting to make it a real challenge for them when Dorothy came up to my desk on tip-toes.

"Lizzie died last night–so the Yoder girls won't be here today. The funeral will be in three days–and even though it didn't come as no surprise, still there's lots to be done.

I could tell from Dorothy's firm stance that I might as well put aside the test until she had her say.

"All her undergarments have to be handmade–and she will be dressed all in white–dress, cape and apron and organdy cap. Most often, and sure with Lizzie, the cape and apron will be the same as she wore on her wedding day."

"Will she be taken to the funeral parlor?"

"They Yoders are pretty conservative. I don't think they'll allow her to be embalmed. Here in Indiana our officials don't much like this, they say for health reasons the dead have to be embalmed. If the family kin git around it someway they will. Sure nobody but them will be allowed to touch her. 'Cause its winter and we don't get too much into town out here, I would venture there won't be no embalming. Ain't right accordin' to our ways. The family will take care of her. The womenfolk comb her hair and dress her."

"Will there be a wake?"

"I don't rightly know exactly what you mean–but 'cause Lizzie was Old Order herself–not her children–I imagine there will be some brothers and sisters sitting up all night beside her coffin."

"What kind of coffin do your people have?"

"Our coffins are made by the menfolk and are usually of pine–they are oiled with a lid that can be slid back to show the upper part of the body–now with Lizzie sure hers won't be lined–some of the more modern ones line it with a white material. The coffin is usually on view in the house and many neighbors, family and friends come in to pay their respects to the family."

"Does the funeral service take place in the house?"

"Don't you remember, we ain't got no churches–it usually begins around nine o'clock in the home and lasts several hours with deacons and Bishops gettin' up and talkin' about the person and preachin' about the times in the Old Testament."

"Is the person buried on the farm?"

"That used to be the way–now the officials of the State don't like it that way and we bury in the cemeteries like other folks but without all the fancy things.

"After the preachin' is finished, the body is viewed once again in the house and then the pallbearers lift up the coffin for it ain't got no side handles and put it on a spring wagon and a team drives away very slowly to the cemetery. The body is followed by a line of slow goin' buggies. Once at the burying place, sometimes the body is viewed for the last time, and then it is let gently down in the already dug hole.

"There ain't no flowers or nothing else except that all go back to the house where the funeral service was. By this time neighbors have prepared a big dinner. We Amish consider death a natural step in life and 'cause we expect to go to Heaven, we are supposed to say we embrace it–life really returns right quick to how it was before except that there is one person less. The women wear black for about a year, if it is someone real close, less time for somebody not so near."

—◆—

After Dorothy finished her contribution to my cultural advancement, I was to receive a far different type of lesson.

Mary came boldly up to my desk and blurted out, "Ma says to tell you that you charged too much."

Momentarily I was taken slightly off balance, "What do you mean, Mary?"

" 'Member yesterday I took my basket home and you said I owed a quarter for the reeds. Ma says that was the price of them when they were wet and they are dry now; they don't weigh that much."

"Your mother is absolutely right. How much did she figure it to be? I am certain she is right."

"Fifteen cents." She slapped down three nickels on my desk.

—◆—

Life in the one-room school is quite as predictable as is that of the farmer's wife–Monday, washing; Tuesday, ironing; Wednesday, prayer meeting; Thursday, quilting; Friday, baking; Saturday, cleaning; and Sunday, church. Everyday in school, too, had our established program but to which change could always be made. Routine, although some may consider it relatively boring, provides a discipline which proves invaluable in later life. Discipline with flexibility are two major building blocks in the character of a child who goes to the likes of Froggy Bottom School.

— ♦ —

The day of "Miss Todd's Tea and Froggy Bottom's Spell-Down" was anticipated with much expectation. Friday morning on that momentous day, all the pupils arrived with an added lustre to their cheeks and hair and with clothes carefully brushed and pressed. Lessons whizzed along–everyone was prepared.

Promptly at 2:00 p.m. Mrs. Bender's Model T pulled into the school yard filled with laughing neighborhood mothers. Mrs. Martin came in right behind with an upright Grandma Mast stiffly at her side. Being Friday, of course, the kitchens that morning had been filled with the heady aromas of baking and each seemed to bring a sample of her culinary skills. This was definitely a day for the ladies–not one man showed up and this was undoubtedly arranged by the women of the community, themselves.

The spell-down went as scheduled with the three judges-referees presiding. I took a back bench. Daniel was chief judge and slowly and distinctly pronounced the word to be spelled. The participant stood apart from his team–first he had to repeat the word, then spell it slowly letter-by-letter, and then again repeat the word. He could change the spelling or correct the spelling before his final pronouncement of the word, but once he said the word twice there could be no change.

Omar, Abner, Charlie and Aaron were eliminated on the first round. This did not come as a surprise to anyone. With all their coaching they had not improved one iota. Bobby went more rounds than anyone thought he would, but stumbled on the word "received."

"He didn't learn the 'lice' rule" whispered Aaron from back of the stove where the downed boy spellers had congregated.

Mary went down with "anticipated."

"That's far too difficult a word for a young'un to spell," was Lucy Michael's comment about her daughter's failure. "I don't know what it means, nor kin I spell it. She's done real fine."

Now, there were only three spellers left—Grace, James and Vilma—and from this trio would be chosen the champion speller of Froggy Bottom who would compete in the township's spelling contest.

The words became harder and harder but still there were three. Finally Grace tripped on the word "illustrated." James was cocky and sure when he was asked to spell "phenomenon" which he carefully pronounced and then spelled "fenonenon" and just as quickly reiterated the word realizing at the same time that he had made a mistake, but, it was too late to change. His error made little Vilma and Mary's team winners. Actually everyone including James was delighted. Sportsmanship in all types of competition is another basic learned in these one-room schools.

Then came the "tea." The community ladies gathered around munching, sipping, chatting and praising their talented children.

Mrs. Martin stood up and said. "I think that a special prize should be given to Vilma today—I suggest that all these baked goods that we haven't eaten be given to her—breads, cookies, buns."

"Mamma is going to be so happy—she hasn't had fresh home-baked goods for ever so long."

"Oh, but there is a prize for the school's Champion." Again my brother Ralph had aided me. He had pressed out in a tin alloy, a circular medal with the punched-in letters "Froggy Bottom Spelling Champion" which he had backed with a safety pin.

As I pinned it on Vilma's tattered sweater, it could have been a diamond brooch—it could not have meant more to her. The child's eyes were radiantly happy.

Those were the last days of January. The boys were still trying to beat their record of sledding to the fence at the edge of the road from the top of the hill. Bobby and Charlie maintained this record. Their scars of December had long since disappeared but now they tried only on conventional sleds and there was no one who was ready to challenge their marks in the snows. They were the champions of Froggy Bottom's Hill!

FEBRUARY

A "shorty" as Sadie Smucker called it, February is probably the most active and stimulating month of the entire school year particularly in the American one-room schoolhouse. It abounds in American history and Romanticism.

The first of the month began during the latter part of the week. On Thursday it was the source of a most profound discussion between Orval and Aaron.

Aaron acting as the know-it-all sage said, "You can't mean you believe in such stuff and nonsense? Imagine a little ground hog comin' out of his hole standing up on his hind legs, sniffin' the air and if the sun is shinin' he goes back into his nest and sleeps for another six weeks. That is childish!"

Orval was unsure of himself particularly when the older boy seemed so positive, "My ma says that if he sees his shadow, we still have lots of winter days ahead of us."

"Old wives' tales."

"My ma ain't an old wife."

"Why don't you ask Miss Todd?"

Diplomacy is one of the first arts a schoolteacher must learn. "Boys I suppose in a way you are both right. Certainly Groundhog Day on February 2nd is one of our American traditions. It is a little fanciful, but it adds color to our heritage. More often than not the farmers have found–and this they have records of–that if the day is sunny there is more harsh winter to follow. I suppose somebody with a good sense of humor thought that it would make it more memorable if a friendly looking ground hog popped out of his burrow to see if he had a shadow on this day.

"Why don't we do some scientific research? We'll keep track if there is sun and shadow tomorrow and how many winter days we have until spring. You two boys and your classmates will be in charge of this project. You'll have to make a wall chart so we can all observe your findings."

Next day at noon the fourth and fifth graders were still on the same subject.

"At ten o'clock the sun was shining–now it's cloudy. Does he or doesn't he see his shadow?"

This momentous question was never fully answered to anyone's satisfaction, but at least a weather chart did go up with both classes jointly in charge.

—◆—

Friday noon I was tidying up my grade book preparing for the weekend, when I felt my desk engulfed. Every girl in the school stood there. Grace stepped forward.

"Miss Todd, we know you are extra busy but this is extra special..." She stopped and started again. "We'd like to discuss this month's program."

"Yes, I know. We have so much American history to review." I felt their faces fall.

"That wasn't exactly what we had in mind. Here we always make a big thing of Valentine's Day and we thought maybe you could get some magazines and fancy paper..."

Gladys broke in, "I can get some wallpaper ends from our neighbor Charlie Kulp who does a lot of hanging for fancy houses in Elkhart."

Mary joined the increasing enthusiasm, "I'll ask Mrs. Martin for some of her old magazines–she takes *Collier's* and *Good Housekeeping*. Maybe she'd let us cut some up."

"Miss Todd, could you ask Mr. K. (they knew about my Goshen benefactor) for a square cardboard box. We always put our Valentines in one secret-like," added Grace.

Monday morning the yellow table was covered with potential Valentines–Sears, Roebuck and colored seed catalogs, *Prairie Farmer*, several household magazines, wallpaper strips, red cloth patches. Besides the requested box Mr. K. had generously donated a big box of waxy crayons for Froggy Bottom School and a package of red construction paper. Grace and her enlisted cohorts soon took charge. She had thoughtfully brought a small bowl, paint brush and flour. With her newly prepared glue she covered the box in white paper (donation from Weaver's Meat Market in Foraker) and pasted on red hearts in various sizes and shapes. A wide slit had been made in the top of the box.

To this a rather disinterested Dorothy said, "That's where everyone puts their card so that nobody knows who sent the Valentine."

— ♦ —

The days outside were miserably cold and sleety but the children were never more content. My monthly copy of *Normal Instructor* was filled with cut-outs and traceable Washington and Lincoln presidential memorabilia. There were at least thirty different sketches depicting the life of Lincoln and I allowed each child to choose the design he wished; the object was to make a biographical booklet of Abraham Lincoln.

Everyone became vitally absorbed in Lincoln's life. Vilma asked me bluntly, "Are you one of his relatives, Miss Todd?"

All I could say was, "Maybe you could say so–but, a lot removed."

As with all studies there are always some that stand out more than others. Not surprisingly one such belonged to James. Rather than choose any pattern from my teacher's manual, he made his own. It was a facsimile of the Ford theater in Washington, D.C. There was a billboard to the right of its entrance. It read: John Wilkes Booth–8 P.M.– April 14, 1865. The title page of the booklet was a mock stage with partially opened curtains between which was carefully scripted and centered in China black ink, "The Dying Thoughts of the Sixteenth President of the United States of America, Abraham Lincoln."

Although James was an ardent admirer of this president he abhorred any kind of violence and cruelty particularly where animals were involved. James knew how to manipulate even when it came to the image of the President of the United States. What I could not fully explain, although I had a good idea, was the reason for the beautiful handwriting. James had never achieved anything much better than a scrawl.

"Daniel was so kind to offer to help me out," was James' offhanded remark to my question.

Flipping the pages, I saw there were few words: "Temperance in All Things"; "Dedicate Oneself to a Cause"; "The Great Solution is Never Achieved Through Violence– I Never Pulled a Trigger on Anything Bigger than a Wild

Turkey"; "The Will of God Prevails" was the closing phrase. The curtains are drawn on the last page.

The little book said much about James. He can not bear that his heroes might have feet of clay. Could he have erased the Civil War, he would have done so. Now he had to be satisfied with a slight remoulding of Lincoln's moral features so that they fit into his preconceived noble statue of him.

Another booklet was equally telling. Abner chose a log cabin as motif for his book cover. Although he basically used the pattern I had, it was his unusual treatment that was so interesting. Meticulously he pasted pieces of collected tree bark on the logs of the cabin, stuffed soft putty between them, put a piece of brown cord in the hole for the door pull and oiled paper at the window. Abner tried to authenticate Lincoln's home in Indiana.

"Early Years" was the title of his work and it was devoted in particular to Lincoln's mother, Nancy Hanks, a natural child (Abner would never have thought of using the word illegitimate even if he had known it) and the rumored story that her unknown father was a Virginian aristocrat (Lincoln's grandfather). Abner portrayed Nancy Hanks not as the hardened embittered pioneer woman so often sketched but as a mystical, ethereal spirit who endowed her son with fathomless strengths. Abner found in Nancy Hanks the source of Lincoln's greatness.

Everyone rushed through their lessons to work on their "special" art as they called Valentines or their Lincoln booklets. The boys apparently were more interested in history than the girls but since secrecy veiled the Valentine box no one could be absolutely certain. One thing was certain— young poets were bursting forth everywhere and there were more variations of "roses are red, violets are blue..." than thought imaginable.

Amidst all this activity I could not help but observe that John Henry spent much time with his head on his desk. Although I did ask him if he were well and received a muffled "yes," I decided my three third graders could handle the situation better than I. Very soon they came back with the ferreted out answer.

"John Henry jist feelin' a bit sorry for hisself," said forthright Norma Jean.

"He don't think that anybody likes him—so he won't get any Valentines," added Anna Mae.

"Don't worry, Miss Todd," interjected ever-positive Clara Sue, "We'll take care of it—John Henry will get more than anybody."

Again my intuition had proven correct. I had an inkling of John Henry's problem and the three little do-gooders were the obvious solution. Again I was to find cooperation, love, sharing so much a part of the atmosphere of the one-room schoolhouse.

— ♦ —

Everyday brings some new twist or surprise in teaching. Arithmetic classes are usually straight forward, not too interesting and at times almost boring. On this particular morning I was discussing insurance rates and claims with the seventh grade. I had taken a hypothetical case of a barn which had been destroyed by fire and was trying to explain the workings of insurance policy payments when I was forced to stop. The room was rocking in raucous whispering. Without hesitation I attacked the sixth grade boys.

"All right, which one of you wishes to tell me why we are having this avalanche of noise? Charlie? James? Robert?"

Although they all looked sheepishly guilty, not one ventured a word. This time I found myself most annoyed and felt that I could no longer allow such blatant disobedience to go unpunished.

"Who is the culprit who started this uproar? And why? Speak up." Again no response.

"If I do not hear an explanation for this uproar the entire school will be punished. Our noon break will be only twenty minutes long."

As expected I did get a response but admittedly a most unexpected one.

"It's 'cause of me." A red-faced Orval with down-cast eyes stood up. "Last summer during church at our place me and another boy went to the barn with matches–the barn caught fire and burned to the ground."

Confession they say is good for the soul, but I felt poor Orval would be paying for this sin for the rest of his life. Tags like "boy-barn-burner" are implacably stuck to one's reputation. Rather than continue the discussion, I dismissed the entire school early for lunch.

After my lunch on this same day, Dorothy approached my desk.

"Miss Todd, I think I'd better do some explainin.' For certain you don't understand near all about what happened today in arithmetic class–that part about the insurance."

Dorothy would never sit down. She leaned over the top of the row of books on the front of my desk.

"Us Amish don't believe in havin' insurance of any kind, anymore than we believe in banks–we don't like others to regulate things we can do for ourselves.

"When such things happen like a barn burnin'—struck by lightning or a match—all our kind goes together and builds another one."

Dorothy gave me one of her rare smiles, "Barn-raisin' is like havin' a big party for us—families from all over, of all ages get together—the women cookin' and talkin'; the men hammerin' and nailin'; and us young'uns runnin' in between havin' a good time."

Dorothy's facial features became serious. She took her self-appointed post of interpreter of the Amish faith very solemnly.

"One of the basic tenets (her choice of words and vocabulary never ceased to amaze me) taught by our Bishops comes direct from the Bible—'if any provide not...for those of his own house, he hath denied the faith and is worse than an infidel.' It is our belief to take care of our own—in sickness, in want, against the ravages (again this word must have been drawn from a sermon) of Nature."

Everyday my own education is being broadened. Many of these farm families may not have understood such highfalutin' words, as they would say, such as social responsibilities but they live "Love thy neighbor as thyself."

—◆—

Vilma, my fifth grader, has returned after three days absence. She looks a bit peaked, but I never ask if she has been ill for the circumstances in her home life have so often proven to be embarrassing for the child.

After Dorothy left, however, the three third graders pulled a rather reluctant Vilma forward with them to my desk.

As usual Norma Jean began, "Miss Todd, you know Vilma has missed school for some days."

For the life of me I could not think what was behind all this well-chosen prattle.

"Vilma has not heard the last couple chapters in *Little Women*," chirped Anna Mae on cue.

"You would like me to lend Vilma the book so she can read for herself where..."

"Oh, no!" broke in an upset Clara Sue. "What we want is for you to re-read little Beth's deathbed scene." She blurted out their well-orchestrated plan and timidly added, "It is so deliciously sad."

These children continually bring a taste of unadulterated innocence into my life.

"The tears make you all clean inside," Norma Jean wisely added, "and Vilma doesn't know this part–it is so lovely–so moving."

On this note I told myself that James was not the only one in my entourage to have theatrical tendencies. Throughout this whole performance, Vilma said not a word only her big eyes registered the nuances and gestures. I consented to the request and was appreciatively thanked with practiced sighs of gratitude from the three third graders.

—◆—

Valentine's Day was very near and a deceptive calm had settled over the schoolroom which I mistakenly attributed to everyone working on last minute details. I, too, was concentrating on desk work when something caused my eye to catch and hold on the sixth and seventh graders. Gladys was sitting bold upright, not moving a muscle. On the far side of her desk, Abner was sketching her, making rapid strokes with a charcoal pencil.

Rather than interrupt this seemingly unscholastic activity, I again put my head down as it appeared harmless enough. Only then did disturbing images begin to flash across my thoughts.

This morning I had seen Bobby in the boy's cloakroom holding high a jar filled with colorless liquid. He said, "I tried it on Flopsie's fur and it worked," as he showed it to James and Charlie.

Then the laughter-restrained-red faces of James and Charlie who were too obviously absorbed in Abner's work were brought to mind. And Bobby—where was he in this scene? His desk was directly behind Gladys but I had not even seen his head.

It all took shape—like a flash I flew to Bobby's desk—but it was already too late. The ends of Glady's long dark braids had both turned a brassy yellow. Bobby had dipped them into his inkwell now filled with his mysterious chemical concoction.

Without a word, I grabbed him by the ear and marched him to the woodshed. I was furious. "How could you?" Bobby's corduroys provided protective padding and the paddling certainly hurt my hand more than his bottom.

As the children had never before seen me so angry, the atmosphere on Bobby's and my return was exaggerated silence. Recitations were whispered for the rest of the day.

Rural news spread rapidly. Several days later Mrs. B. was carefully dicing up potatoes for soup—she is very proud of her kitchen skills.

"The Fuller Brush man stayed to dinner (noontime) today—he ate two pieces of my crumb pie—said it was the best in Elkhart County."

Next came the onions. The butter and milk already set on the counter. Once the ingredients were all on the back of the stove bubbling ever so slowly in a big covered pot,

Mrs. B. wiped her hands and finally got to the point of the day.

"Heard you got right excited about Gladys' bleached braids?"

"It was a matter of trust. I never thought any of the children would do such a thing."

"Careful, Missy. You don't want to get a reputation of a hysterical female."

"What about Gladys' parents? What must they be thinking?"

"Spoke to Gladys' ma at prayer meeting. She weren't upset. Said it was time for Gladie's locks to be trimmed anyway. She said her husband had said it weren't nothing for the young schoolmarm to get her water hot about as the boys were just funning."

I blushed red. Perhaps I had lost my focus.

Certainly this point was to be driven home on Valentine's Day. The three third graders took over the distribution of the cards. These three are into everything and everywhere and no one ever seems to challenge the rights they so royally accept as theirs. Valentines began piling high on little John Henry's desk. His crossed eyes glistened.

When I leaned over and asked him if he had sent any, he whispered back, "Yes."

"To whom?"

"Sadie." Never has a young lover looked more smitten.

The next one was a surprise–it was Daniel's desk. It would seem that every girl in Froggy Bottom, little and big, had a crush on him. The more cards that came, the deeper the flush on his downy cheeks. Never once during the entire afternoon did he dare to lift his eyes.

Although I did not count my cards, I am quite certain I received one from each child. Froggy Bottom pupils are indeed an industrious group—not one card given on this day was "store bought."

But the biggest, best and most surprising was too large to fit into the Valentine box. A huge red cardboard folder was addressed to "Bobby." Inside a young woman leaned over a balcony, Romeo and Juliet fashion, with her long braids drooping from above to the ground as her young lover looked upward. On the tips of her tresses had been pasted Glady's bleached ones. Across the scene written in large bold letters, "All My Love." If Bobby had not been punished sufficiently before, he now reaped more than his ample share. He was the brunt of teasing taunts from all the other boys and was thoroughly and completely mortified.

Who can understand the ways of females at any age?

To put a fitting end to this entire tale, Bobby brought me a gift. Still tantalized by his male friends, he meekly handed me a brown paper sack.

"From my pa."

Robert's father did fine carpentry work during the winter months. Inside was a beautifully polished and smooth and very strong wooden paddle. Crudely written on a piece of lined notebook paper was the message, "This will be better than your hand. Use it well. Joel Hartman."

I carefully showed it to the entire room telling them who had presented it to me and then proudly hung it from a nail on the side of the library.

—◆—

The days continued to be blustery. Usually with bad weather, school attendance was high but for the past several days all the older boys had either not come at all or appeared sporadically during the day.

"It's harness time," came Omar's answer.

His brother Abner amplified, "Every winter usually at this time we have to grease and repair the harnesses for the comin' work year."

"That means all the horse trappings," interjected Chris. "Everything from bits and bridles, blinders, reins, breast collars, girths, cruppers, breechings, traces–everything is gone over that is used to gear the horses."

"All the leather has to be worked and rubbed until it is soft," Aaron held up his bleeding, chapped hands, "it's good for these, too."

Dorothy who is normally hovering about, came over and took one of Aaron's hands in hers.

"Land of Goshen! They look like raw meat. Tell your ma to rub some Paine King salve into them. If she ain't got any, tell me and my grandma will send some over."

The boy's hands had never known gloves nor mittens. The crusts across the knuckles had broken open and bled as had the fingers around his nails.

Again Dorothy who is such a good-hearted soul said, "That yellow salve is the best. I used it on Prim's teats. Her bag was so big and sore, she kicked and stormed so no one could really milk her, that is until I used Paine King. The label says it right, 'good for Man or Beast.' "

Being in one of her chatty moods, Dorothy added, "Don't expect the boys to be in regular attendance after the harness fixings. Then their pa's goin' give them a treat."

One never questions Dorothy's verbal launches. One waits.

"The farmers take their animals and products including some household goods to the auction barn. Locally we usually go to Wakarusa but should any family have kin in Shipshewannee (Shipshewana), they go for a visit there 'cause the auction is bigger and better.

"Winter auction days are jist for men and boys–they might sort of compare to 'English' fairs–the men jaw and swap stories. To get the best price be it for animals, corn, wheat or hay is kinda a game with them. For their boys the fathers take it real serious–it is like a learnin' school. The pa points out the good and the bad–moldy hay, smutty corn, beetle-ridden wheat, and particularly the weaknesses, faults and defects in the animals–cows, horses, hogs, whatever they might be seein' in the auction circle.

"The men sit 'round in seats above a sand covered circle. The animal is brought in and shown off–sometimes they have studied it before the auctioneer starts. He usually knows all the men and their secret ways of bidding. At times the father lets his son take over the biddin' for a spell– to give him his head as they say. The boys come back every year puffed up and feelin' manly. 'Tis normal for the boys to miss 'round three days of school."

During the auction days there was a big void in the schoolroom. We did have one unforgettable event which caused the evacuation of the school. Little Amos arrived late and alone. He was a most unhappy little boy for Orval, his brother, had been allowed to go to Wakarusa with his father. To question or rebel against a parent's decision is unheard of among the Amish–and the Millers are Amish. Still Amos' mother, as mothers all over the world, could not but have noticed her baby boy's sadness.

Of course, all this came from Dorothy. Amos told his Mother he had found a beautiful black and white kitty-cat in the barn and he was going to try to tame it.

Being more busy than usual with the men folks goin' off to the auction and being nearly laid up in bed with a severe head cold, all Anna Miller said to her son was to be careful for cats can be dangerous.

Supposedly little Amos jocularly replied, "Not this one–she seems to like me–she walks real slow and doesn't seem to mind about anything."

To make a long story short, Amos apparently met with some degree of success with his "kitty-cat." When he entered, all the other pupils were already in their seats. The stench which exuded from around his little body was breathtakingly vile.

"Skunk!" was the big cry from the entire room.

Fortunately it was a bright and sunny morning. We marched everyone outside and aired the schoolroom. I sent Amos home with Dorothy to explain to his mother what had happened and why he was being returned home.

Amos was in big tears. Little Amish children do not cry easily, but he had an emotion-filled morning.

"She was so nice–then she lifted her tail and sprayed with this yellow stuff."

— ♦ —

Most of the children had chosen the silhouette of George Washington to make their biographical booklet of the first President of the United States. Although the members of the lower three grades were considered too young to join in this project, they were very active in their interest and participation.

I overheard John Henry earnestly questioning Sadie, "How could that man be the father of a whole country?"

Wisely, I decided not to interfere. Certainly I would have only muddied John Henry's mental waters more.

It was Vilma's question to Alma which quite took me aback, "Do you think George Washington was Amish?"

Alma, who is always a bit bristly about her religion, didn't know whether the older girl was saying this in jest or not. When she saw Vilma was serious, she took an almost condescending stance.

"Of course, not. Don't you know anything about American History?"

"I mean 'cause he wore his hair long."

"First of all, it was the fashion of the day. Next he was married, and he ain't got no beard like any Amish with a wife. Not only that, his hair is tied back showing his ear–our men don't ever knowingly show their ears; they wear their hair just to the top of the collar a bit like William Penn."

Whether this last remark was part of Alma's whimsical fluff that she occasionally pulls out, I don't know. Certainly she, too, thoroughly enjoys having an audience–a point which brought her into a rather unfavorable light several days later.

Grace was holding court. It was one of those miserably cold rainy days when none of the girls wanted to venture out. They had gathered around the little yellow table.

"Was he handsome?"

On this note I picked up my ears as the girls did not often talk openly about the opposite sex.

"I couldn't really say–but he was very talented."

"What did he do?"

"He played scale after scale."

For some not-so-apparent reason on my part, there exists a very deep-seated antipathy between Grace and Alma. Although the latter was several grades behind, they were nearly the same age and Alma plunged into the other's territory without any hesitation.

"Are you still talkin' about that piano tuner, Grace?"

Grace tossed her head haughtily and pretended not to have heard. "He had such long artistic fingers."

"The only reason you're goin' on so is to remind us all you got a piano in your house."

From my own observation I felt there was a grain of truth in Alma's comment. Grace, who considered herself the only "refined" pupil, was becoming definitely annoyed which only added to Alma's goading taunts.

"Did he crook his finger when he drank his tea?"

Grace had been telling of the wonderful lunch her mother had prepared for the piano tuner. From one of Mrs. B.'s parleys I learned it was an expected gesture on the part of the rural housewife to invite any itinerant worker or visiting tradesman to share a meal with the family. It becomes a festive occasion and as news is always at a premium, it gives the family an opportunity to question about events happening elsewhere. And to entertain the piano tuner would certainly be considered a social achievement locally.

Dorothy with aplomb, walked over and drew Alma aside whispering loudly, "'Tis not humility you are showing, but pride and pretension."

To my utter surprise, Alma returned without a word to her seat and meekly sat down. When I came home that evening Mrs. B. gave me a fuller explanation of this day's happening.

"Humility is supposed to be one of the Amish people's basic religious blocks."

"Dorothy's words were an admonition. In her eyes Alma had been a very disobedient, sinful child."

141

"My impression before I began teaching was that the Amish people were docile—in town they were often referred to as the 'gentle folk.' "

"Balderdash is what I would be calling most city folk's talk. They don't have any idea about life in the country."

Mrs. B. always did at least two things at the same time. Her physical actions often related more than her words. This evening she sprinkled a wooden chopping board with a fine dust of flour then she adroitly flipped a long yellow roll of dough out of its cloth-wrap onto the kitchen plank.

"There ain't nothing Eli likes better—beef and noodles."

Using a wide-bladed knife, she deftly began a precise rhythmic cutting.

Whack, Whack. The falling circles of yellow dough never varied in width.

"Country folk, all kinds of us plain people including the Amish, are hardly what one can call 'gentle.' Here it is always a question of survival."

Whack, Whack.

"It makes a person hard—or maybe more rightly we eliminate all things unnecessary from our lives; the folderol that clutters up the lives of the city folk—we are all God-fearing people—we expect the coming of the Lord, but we don't jist sit around waiting—we get our work done—we live and work together trying to observe the ways of the Good Book."

Whack, Whack.

"Never think the Amish are kin to angels. Their forefathers—like most of ours here in the country came from Europe, mostly Germany and Switzerland. If you ever get a chance to see any of their Bishops, they look as if they walked out of the pages of the Old Testament."

Whack, Whack.

"That's mainly their teaching–they are and act like the patriarchs of old–thunder and lightning, hell's fire and brimstone are their disciplinary tools. They suffer no stuff and nonsense from any of their young–or old. Probably that was something that little Alma set herself thinking about. Would the Bishops find out?"

Whack, Whack.

"Gentle, never–they follow the way of Moses–and women are not particularly in good favor at the best, being taught to be submissive to their menfolk."

Whack, Whack.

—◆—

The month was nearing the end. No one could decide from our Groundhog chart whether it would be an early spring or not. During the past week the days had been quite mild and some of the boys were talking about doing some early plowing.

On this particular day, I was pronouncing spelling words to the third grade. Much to my surprise, I had to discipline Susie Cripe of the second grade. She was flashing the words on a card to Clara Sue who is not too quick. Remarkably all of Susie's words were correct. I was in the midst of trying to tell her gently that this was not to be done when I was interrupted by a thumping knock on the front door.

My visitor was no less than the County Superintendent of Schools, David Kreider. A big man, Mr. Kreider, shook my hand heartily leaving it absolutely limp. As I had never met him before and as the visiting Superintendent experience was also new to me, I began explaining my curriculum outline to him. This he soon squashed.

"Don't bother your pretty little head about all those things. I'll just pull up a chair and listen a spell."

Rather unsure of myself, I continued with third grade spelling, happy to see that Susie had taken the hint and was offering no added help. Next I went to fourth grade geography. This certainly was not my most brilliant set of pupils, but I felt that I could not take a class out of order.

I asked Orval to pull down the map of the United States. Next in absolute trepidation, I asked if either could repeat the names of the New England States. Both raised their hands. I selected Alma.

She began slowly but surely, "Maine, New Hampshire, Vermont..." I stopped her.

"Orval, do you think you can name their state capitals." This was a most dangerous gesture on my part even though geography was Orval's favorite subject.

He, too, began slowly, "Augusta, Concord, Monpeller..."

"Montpelier," I corrected.

"Massachusetts," continued Alma.

"Boston."

"Rhode Island."

Orval thought a long time before coming out with, "Providence."

"Connecticut."

"Hartford."

"Now I am going to indicate with the pointer a state and I want you to name it, alternating turns."

Here, Mr. Kreider broke in. "Wonderful, Miss Todd. I can see from your style and the room itself." His hand made a wide sweep. "Never saw a blackboard decorated with capital and small letters of the alphabet before—excellent—and the curtains at the windows with their colorful figures pinned on. Yes, it is evident you had your training afar. Keep up your good work."

I smiled rather weakly. I was still wobbly from my fourth graders brilliant performance. Never would I be able to understand it–never had they so shone.

And as for my special teacher's training, if Mr. Kreider only knew that most of it was received in my own home. With nine children, very little money but lots of love and encouragement and with the firm belief that education was the key to success and happiness in life, my parents provided the basis for all my training. I could not remember when we did not "play school"–we each had our crock to sit on and my mother let us use their green bedroom door to write on with chalk. I had always loved school and learning. My wonderful father had seen this and it was he who took me by the hand when I was five years old and asked the local teacher if I could attend school. She agreed if I did not cause any trouble. Somewhere along the line, these home instructions must have benefited us all–out of nine children there were four to become teachers.

I hardly thought any of this would interest the Superintendent of Schools so I simply said, "Good-bye."

MARCH

"March sure is roarin' in like a lion," were Omar's opening morning words to me. He was helping to stoke the stove for the day. The wind howled and angrily whipped our faces as we carried in the day's wood supply from the shed.

"That means it will go out like a lamb."

Weather is always a good conversational subject but among the country people it is taken as a serious study. Planting and harvesting crops are done according to the signs of the moon.

Like Mrs. B. said, "Nobody would ever consider planting their spring crops without a good almanac read first– there ain't a house that don't have a copy of the *Old Farmer's Almanac*–it's the most read book here after the Bible."

Certainly these not quite spring days seemed to energize the children. One could almost feel the electrical current surging through their young bodies.

One mid-day early in the month, James, full of vim and vigor, stomped up to my desk. From his facial expression I knew this was going to be a very serious conference.

"Miss Todd, do you realize we are terribly behind schedule?"

With James one never knew what to expect. To wait was the only answer.

"Because you are still considered 'new,' my committee and I..."

If James had a committee which I seriously doubted, they certainly would be nothing more than mute puppets.

"...thought you would probably need some advice."

Still I waited.

"It has been the custom in the past to give a Last Day program...."

"Great minds run in the same channel, James. Look at this outline I have roughly sketched out for such an occasion."

The deflated little boy carefully studied the paper I had handed him. I had been told by Mrs. B. that it was usual to present all of the accomplishments the students had made during the year on the last day. I had already added a few innovative flourishes of my own.

James diplomatically said, "It looks good. Have you decided on the date–this is most important."

I was slightly taken aback by this comment.

"I thought it was to be held on the last day of school."

"True, in the past it has been–but my committee and I have given it some serious thought..."

I had to turn my head to one side. Smiles were not in order. This was a very grave situation!

"April is a very unreliable month. There is much work to do on the farm during this time of the year. Therefore not many from the families are present on the last day. During the daytime everyone is too busy with the work of early spring. It's <u>our</u>..." He stressed this last word.

"...idea that we prepare a program on the last day of this month at night."

"But, James..." was all that I was able to utter.

"We have it all figured out. Already I have the lanterns and a hay rack. That stage we had at Christmas was pretty awful–and dangerous."

There could be no denying that James and "his committee" had worked out all the physical details for a night program very well.

"So now all we have to do is get the program itself together."

From his manner, I concluded that he thought I could accomplish this. In order not to discourage his boyish enthusiasm, I brought the proposal of the last day's program, which I presented as James' suggestion, to the entire school's attention that very afternoon. The idea of having a program at night was original and all were wildly interested. Soon the room was a-buzz. Plans and designs were coming in from right and left. To calm the atmosphere, I proposed that they all think over their ideas and tomorrow we would work out a program. I reminded them we did not have too much time–the end of March was only three weeks away.

My own principal aim was to demonstrate to the parents all the items the children had made throughout the school year. I was very proud of what I called Froggy Bottom's Arts and Crafts Workshop–weaving, knitting, crocheting, finger-painting, collage, clay models, homemade birdhouses, sketches, paintings–the children had worked in all these forms. It had also been my decision that the pupils must choose the work that was to represent each category and that no one could be shown in more than one division. I also wanted each pupil to be represented.

The next day there seemed to be discontent and grumbles from every nook and corner.

"This is quite impossible." Gladys threw both arms in the air. "How does Miss Todd ever expect us to choose only one item from a person and still have a good display. Everything that Mary does is always the best."

James was the only one who seemed to be working smoothly. He and his group–no longer did "the committee" exist–were already reading the short adaptation that James had written for his *Tom Sawyer* scene. The role of Tom was to be played by Bobby and Huckleberry Finn by Charlie.

"Are these two boys the only ones you are having?"

"No. Jim is also in it but he is a 'Black boy'; Orval would like to play him but I know his ma would never allow him to have his face blackened, let alone be in a play. So I've almost decided on Vilma.

"Will she allow you to soot her face?"

"Oh, sure. My real problem is Aunt Polly. I would like to have Mary play her but the girls are having such casting difficulties, I'll have to wait until they decide before I can make my final choice."

This was the first I realized the girls, too, were planning to present a skit.

"Do you know what the girls are planning, James?"

"Oh, sure. A scene from Louisa Mae Alcott's *Little Women*–Beth's deathbed. All the girls want to be Beth and no wants to be the Mother."

"Who's directing?"

"That's a good question. It was the third graders' idea. Of course, they are too young to produce such a show."

Where did James come by his sophisticated terminology?

"The last time I heard, Grace is directing–but even she wants a role. Women never can make up their minds!"

From all these corner confabs, I gathered that my first, second and fourth graders plus the big boys (except the sixth graders) still needed to have their parts assigned for the last day program. This would prove to be quite a task.

— ◆ —

Undoubtedly it was wishful thinking on my part when I saw the big farm boys huddled together–maybe, they, too, had found a means of group expression for the program.

"Jonie Ramer started to tap his trees last week."

"Ain't his grove still too young?"

"Yeh, Chris. My pa says sugar maples have to be at least forty years old 'fore they're tapped.

The school program had never entered these boys' minds–they were all preoccupied with maple syrup making.

Always respectful Chris asked, "Do you know anything about maple syrup making, Miss Todd?"

"Not really. All I know is that there is nothing more delicious than eating a stack of sour-milk pancakes topped with butter and swimming in country-made maple syrup."

"Boys, we gotta explain this doin' to our teacher."

Abner began, "It's that time of the year when the sap starts to run in sugar maple trees. About halfway up the trunk a hole is drilled so a small spout can be put in–a little bucket is hung on it to collect the sap."

"Tell her about the grove and sugar camp," broke in Omar.

"Be patient. I'll get there. Most trees used here are of the sugar maple kind–some people mix maples but most people here like to keep their taste pure. Groves have been planted and when they are mature, a sugar camp is set up each year during the month of March."

Aaron chimed in, "Tell her about sleepin' over."

"Right. In many of the camps, the men have gone together and built a small shack where they can catnap and fix some vittles. The collected sap has to be boiled down to make the maple syrup. The fires have to be kept goin' and the sap stirred off and on. It ain't hard work–sorta slow and borin' but the men look forward to gettin' away for overnight particularly the young ones–there lots of horsin' 'round, too."

Chris added, "The maple sap is cooked, really evaporated in huge kettles."

"How do you know when it is finished?" was my question.

"Experience, I suppose. The lighter the color, the better the syrup is considered to be. It is reckoned that one quart of maple syrup should rightly weigh about two and three-quarter pounds or eleven pounds to the gallon."

The exchange was now between Chris and myself.

"Is this a money-making project for any one farmer or for the community?"

"Not really, Miss Todd. We like to do for our own but when you get to sellin' products, particularly foodstuffs, there is always lots of regulations that you got to go by and us country people don't like to do all that bothering just for a little money.

"How much does a tree yield?"

"That's also right difficult to say. Daniel's father who probably has got the biggest stand of sugar maples around, once told my pa that he considered it a good average take to get three pounds per tree."

Daniel who never ventured much to any conversation did say, "Pa also said he has had some trees that would yield up to as much as twenty pounds."

"Don't the women do anything with the making of maple syrup?"

"No. This is considered men's work."

"Can the community use all this maple syrup in one year's time?"

"That you can be sure, Miss Todd. The womenfolks use lots in their cookin' and bakin.' My ma says it is much sweeter and healthier. She figures three-quarter of a cup of maple syrup equals about a cup of regular, store-bought sugar. Farm people don't like to buy store things. My ma says she never knows what they put in all those packages."

As if to say that Chris had become too long-winded, Aaron chirped, "Wait till you try some maple sugar candy. Grandma Mast makes the best."

—◆—

The following day I called Daniel to my desk. I seemingly could not put the rest of the last day's program together. Could Daniel help me out? Henry Wadsworth Longfellow's poem "Paul Revere's Ride" would be an ideal way of grouping most of the big boys if I could count on Daniel's support.

Much to my delight Daniel said he would be happy to drill the boys and recite the opening stanzas of the poem himself. This was a big relief.

We were bent over the book dividing up the stanzas, some thirteen in all, among five other boys. I had decided to include Orval among the older lads. This would make him very proud. Orval was to take the stanza beginning, "It was twelve by the village clock...." Aaron, the one beginning, "It was one...." And Omar, "It was two by the village clock..." The rest of the stanzas would be given alternately to Chris and Abner. This had always been the boys' favorite poem and with Daniel's coaching they would soon have it letter perfect. While we were going over the last details, Dorothy joined us. She just stood silent for some time.

"Miss Todd, I gotta talk to you."

How well I know this crisis tone. "I'll be right with you. Daniel and I were just finishing."

He immediately turned and walked erectly away. "Now, what do you want to tell me, Dorothy?"

Still silent, she pushed out a brown paper parcel. "For you from Grandma."

Perplexed, I opened the package to find within the box, two star-shaped candies.

"Maple sugar. Grandma thought you might like to taste them."

"Thank you. Did your grandmother make these candies?"

"Yes. It's real easy. You take two cups of syrup, boil it over a low slow heat without stirrin'—boil 'til it gets thready. Let it cool for about an hour. Then add a teaspoon of vanilla, beat 'til it becomes light, fluffy and hard enough to mold—that's all."

"That's all very interesting, Dorothy, but is this what was so urgent to speak to me about?"

"No."

"Well, then?"

"Miss Todd, it's real difficult for me."

Another long silence and then the plunge. "Vilma's mother went to see Mrs. Martin 'cause she didn't know what else to do. Mrs. Martin is often considered very severe and stern, but she does know how to solve problems. Vilma and Norman have not been in school all week not 'cause they are sick in the usual way."

Dorothy certainly was not making the situation very clear but I knew she would have to tell whatever she was trying to explain in her own manner.

"Mrs. Martin went to see my grandma and told her about the situation. Mrs. Martin has great respect for my grandmother's opinion. At first Mrs. Martin, I guess, was real upset–mostly about the children here in the school and particularly her James. Grandma calmed her down and said many worse things have happened, and she shouldn't make anymore fuss as everything now was taken care of."

Dorothy's story was becoming more complicated and less clear as it went along. My mind was going in circles imagining everything from the Black Plague to pregnancy which I knew was impossible.

"Grandma actually went with Mrs. Martin to the Knox house. Probably they gave Vilma's mother a good talkin' to and then helped her scrub the house with Lysol. I know Grandma wore real old clothes when she went there and when she came back she put them all in disinfectant to soak in the big washing tub."

Would Dorothy ever get to the point?

"Grandma told Mrs. Martin that it should not be a gossipy subject in the community–'course everybody's bound to know sooner or later. But, she, Grandma, did say you should be told and Mrs. Martin agreed, before Norman and Vilma come back to school.

Finally I had to say something, "So what did your Grandmother say to tell me?"

Dorothy was not to be deterred in her telling of this account. "Grandma said that although we don't have any visiting nurse here in the country like they do in city schools, Grandma and Mrs. Martin both know that the Knox children are now alright. They gave them the treatment themselves."

"What treatment?"

"Well–they shaved their heads and rubbed their scalps with kerosene. Now they both wear clean knit stocking caps that Mrs. Martin gave them."

I gasped, "You mean the Knox children had head lice!"

"That's right."

The next day both Knox children reappeared. Children being the marvelous creatures they are said nothing about the smelly stocking caps. It was James who truly put everyone at their ease.

"Vilma, I would never have thought of it–but, now with your hair clipped you will make a perfect Jim. What a great idea you've had."

After this hurdle, we still had more problems with the program. Finally it was decided that Beth would be played by Clara Sue as she was the smallest of the three third graders and the most devoted to the deathbed scene. Jo was to be played by Gladys because of her tomboyish qualities. Mary was to be Mrs. March and also, after much persuasion on James' part, to be Aunt Polly in the *Tom Sawyer* skit.

Tempers were flying between the temperamental directors, James and Grace.

"If you had gotten your act together and thought out your situation, we wouldn't have all these problems today. The only boys who can possibly play the part of Laurie would be either Bobby or Charlie and they are both tied up. That's it!"

"They're not refined enough anyway."

"My suggestion is to cut Laurie out altogether. You don't even have a girl who could play him."

What James said was only too true. Not enough foresight had been put into the choice of this scene. But play it, the girls of Froggy Bottom would and with great fervor! The last most unlikely castings were finally made with Anna Mae selected to be Amy and Norma Jean to play the eldest March sister, Meg.

—♦—

The days are becoming noticeably longer. The farmers have begun to haul and spread manure on the fields as can be attested by the penetrating odors and the evident signs on the heavy work shoes of the older boys. Everyone is tired of being cooped up inside. Still the days remain a bit too miserable to get more than a breathe of fresh air.

Everyone is occupied with studying their parts and practicing plus all the added duties the forthcoming program entails. The curtains and blackboard have to be redecorated for spring and the program. Everyone by now knows what they have to do. Abner is working on a new picture that is termed "The Masterpiece"–birds, flowers and the Indiana landscape in the spring. He has a critical and ever present audience. Then in each window sill there is a potted daffodil bulb. These are watched over and watered by the first and second graders. On this subject there is much pessimism. The consensus is that they will never flower in time for the program. Only little Sadie keeps saying, "You gotta have faith–they will bloom for our program."

Grace, Mary, James and Bobby are in charge of designing the program cover. There have been many meetings around the yellow table but to date nothing has as yet materialized.

One of the innovations I have brought to Froggy Bottom is a bird-feeder. My brother Ralph built one that he fitted to the southeast window. The children love to stand inside and watch the birds feed. I found a book on birds which is kept on the yellow table alongside a notebook in which any new bird seen is recorded.

Aaron and Omar are the most knowledgeable bird-watchers and they consider themselves custodians of this project. They bring in crushed corn and wheat and always have a piece of suet hanging in the tray.

On this particular day, Omar had a request which I suggested that he himself present to the entire school.

"We gotta a problem. The birds right now need special care. 'Cause there was a cold start to March, it means that the birds ain't got no way of gettin' food naturally. Their food sources have come to an end. Now this bad weather can hold back flowers. This is a gap between seasons and if we don't put some extra food out many little birds could starve. What I would like is for everybody to ask their ma to give a few dried flower seeds, anything birds could eat, even a few berries from a jar would help."

Omar had never been heard to make such a speech. He sat down exhausted.

It was on that same day his companion also made his mark. Aaron who is very small for his age always manages to be housed in a pair of overalls that are several sizes too big for him. Today it was his turn to replenish the bird-feeder which is in a protected recess on the south side of the school.

I was sitting at my desk when I noticed that all the girls were crowded around the window and giggling naughtily. Finally I, too, had to see what was drawing their attention to the window area for I knew it was not the birds.

Down below on the outside was a pirouetting little Aaron gaily cavorting up and down and doing a sleight-of-hand gesture over his pants' opening flap from which stuck out a corner of his red handkerchief. When the girls saw me they scattered like frightened rabbits, and when Aaron looked up and only saw my face in the window, he went dead white. I only had to shake my index finger at him and mouth the word "No." Aaron then became as red as the corner of his exposed handkerchief. That was little Aaron's excursion into the field of sex and my only experience with the subject while in the one-room school system.

—♦—

"They say the 21st is the beginning of Spring–still frightfully nippy out I find." Mrs. B. gave a tug to my neck scarf. "Don't want you to get the croup. These days are deceptive–gotta be careful not to catch any bugs."

That day in school my second grader Emma Stutzman, who never utters a peep, came timidly up to my desk and asked, "What's a paraguay?"

Baffled I asked her to repeat her question. "What is a paraguay?" she again said, most distinctly.

"Emma, could you tell me how you heard this word used?"

The little girl looked at me in disbelief; teachers are supposed to know everything. "My mother's cousin has been away many years and she's goin' come home from a paraguay."

Then I understood all. Mrs. B. had indicated that many of the younger people belonging to the Mennonite faith had become missionaries.

Then and there, I decided to devote the entire morning to Emma and the study of Paraguay. The children love these impromptu programs which are rare but often enough to break a depressing monotony.

The big map of South America was pulled down and I sat Emma on a small chair on the platform behind my desk. Then I assigned James and Gladys to search for material on the country in our books in the library; in the meantime all the rest of the fourth, fifth, sixth and seventh graders were searching through their geography books to find out all they could about this South American country. Vilma, Aaron and Omar were to discuss the history and social conditions; Chris and Mary, the physical aspects of the country; Orval and Alma were to talk about agriculture with an emphasis on the country's flora; Charlie and Bobby would enumerate the wild animals; Grace and Abner were to discuss religion and education. After each delivered their discussion there was to be a question period by the other students. This would be led by Daniel, Dorothy, James and Gladys.

Although the older ones supposedly were to be the ones to ask the difficult questions, it was little Emma who asked the first question which rather stumped the group.

"How do they talk down there?"

"Like us I suppose," retorted Omar rather superiorly.

"No, that's not right. They speak Spanish," James was to correct.

"Are their Indians like ours?" came bright-eyed Susie's query.

On and on it went. Everyone was deeply involved. Probably Froggy Bottom is the only one-room school in Indiana with such a thorough knowledge of this South American country and all because a little second grader had asked, "What is a paraguay?"

—◆—

The weather has begun to be somewhat milder, still the winds rage and now the rains have also begun. It was on one of these rainy mornings that little Aaron entered looking like a woebegone waif, tired and soaked through and through.

In response to my questions, Aaron mumbled, "That ewe has to be the most stupid animal that God ever created."

Standing near the hot stove Mary, his sister, and I were pulling off his wet clothes and hanging them up to dry.

"Soaked to the skin. Ma goin' be mighty upset with you. Your new mittens are near ruined. You can't save them all."

Aaron was never intimidated by his sister. "It is written that Jesus 'shall gather the lambs in his arm.'"

"You and your Bible spouting, Aaron—you sure goin' end up a preacher if your naughty ways don't get hold of you first."

Now seated on a small stool near the heat and wrapped in the blanket that I had months before brought from home for just such a purpose, Aaron became more talkative.

"There was a whole six acres fenced in. That ewe had to give birth surrounded by hedges. Do you know where she decided to have her young? Exactly right over a puddle of icy water."

By this time the little girls from the first three grades had joined us. I then realized that they all thought Aaron was rather interesting, being a gentle kind of a boy.

"What happened to the baby?" asked Susie.

"Got her behind the stove in the kitchen, my sister Bessie takin' care of her—I ran here 'cause I didn't want Ma to see me."

"Do you think it will live?" asked Emma.

"They're pretty strong. They got the wish. As God wills."

Aaron had now become the oracle on lambing and lamb care. A barrage of giggling girlish questions began.

"Why are you so cruel to the lambies?"

Aaron eyes popped, "Cruel. Me?"

"Well, maybe not you–but why do you cut off the little one's tails? They and I always cry each spring when they do it." Clara Sue began sniffling into her handkerchief.

"My pa explained it all–sometimes you gotta be mean to be kind."

"What do you mean, 'mean'?" Norma Jean could not stand being left out of this discussion.

"If you don't cut off their tails their own animal dirt collects in the wool under the tail. Sheep don't–can't–clean themselves like some animals–dogs or cats. When the hot sun comes, the flies gather there–it is not healthy for the animal. Like Pa says, the long tail is a breeding ground for disease."

Again, kindhearted Clara Sue whimpered, "Can't there be some other way that don't hurt so much–they cry so."

"I only know what my pa says–it's much quicker, it's less painful to 'whack.' The tail, where it's cut off, bleeds good–this sorta of washes away any nasty stuff. Then it drys like a sealer. It's all natural."

Now Anna Mae added, "Ain't there a new idea with rubber-bands or something–so that the tail will eventually drop off."

"Oh, that sounds much better," sighed Clara Sue.

"Wrong. Often the poor little one dies 'cause infection sets in and it's annoyed for days rather than having pain for a few minutes."

Again Clara Sue whined, "It's so sad to hear and see them cry."

For the first time little first grader Katie ventured, "You don't have to watch, Clara Sue."

— ♦ —

With everyone thinking about the program—never had there been any night performance at Froggy Bottom—the township's spelling competition had been quite forgotten that is until I received a notice from the Trustee's office that our representative should be at the Harrison Center School at two o'clock on April 6th. I mentally groaned. Vilma had won our own Spelling Bee and therefore qualified to be Froggy Bottom's delegate. Far from actually being our most scholarly speller, she now would even be more handicapped with her physical appearance. Her hair was now a short half-inch long stubble. What could be done in less than two weeks time?

At noon I decided to broach the subject with the older girls. I called Vilma, Gladys, Grace, Mary and Dorothy to my desk. Perhaps they would have some fashion ideas.

I began gently, "I just received notice of the annual Spelling Bee..."

Dorothy always quick to grasp a situation, "Oh, I see we have a bit of a problem."

Everyone without saying a word, including Vilma, realized the crux of the matter.

Grace, the most fashion conscious of the group offered, "Maybe we could attach a big hair bow atop Vilma's head."

"Miss Todd, do you think that a curling iron could make any impression or is her hair still too short?"

I never had the opportunity to answer as Vilma spoke up, "I think I've the perfect answer—that is if it don't upset nobody. I'll go Amish. I can wear a white covering over my head and no will know the difference.

While almost everyone including myself became voiceless, Dorothy clapped her hands. "Great! I'll outfit you out. You can wear my green dress and black stockings. This, we won't tell the Bishops!"

Whether "Going Amish" can be an acceptable solution I still rather doubt but my Froggy Bottom students once again did teach me a valuable lesson. No situation or problem is without an answer particularly when all work together to resolve it.

—◆—

This is the last week of March. On Friday night is to be our end of the year program. Everyone is experiencing bouts of tummy butterflies and plain stage fright.

Although ten white sailor hats finally were made and fitted along with ten wooden paddles fashioned by Bobby Hartman's father, Grace is still nearly beside herself with the ten from the first three grades. They are supposed to be singing in rounds "Row, Row, Row Your Boats."

On stage the children's Sunday school chairs borrowed by faithful Eli B. from the Southwest church have been tied together to serve as boats. Three have been made with the third-graders as their Captains. Norma Jean's crew had been Sadie and John Henry–the principal difficulty here was that J.H. could not keep in the same oaring rhythm as the others.

Charlie came up with Grace's solution to this. "Put him in the prow with his hand to his forehead looking for land."

Clara Sue is Captain of the second boat with Susie, Amos and Katie. Now with John H. in the prow, Susie has been sent to Norma Jean's boat. Still Number Two Boat can not come in on its round cue.

Boat Number Three has Anna Mae at its helm with Emma and Norma as rowers. Row they can, but sing they can't. They forget the words, they are off-key, but they are loud.

—◆—

Finally the Big Night arrived. The schoolhouse never has had so many guests–eight p.m. and there was not a seat to be found. Everyone in the community was present. The young fellows were sitting on the window sills beside the daffodils which were blooming.

I looked at James–if he were wearing a vest, the buttons would have popped. He was so proud and rightly so. Fifteen lanterns lit the room beautifully in a soft warm glow. The room had been transformed–it had a regal elegance. Even the yellow table appeared handsome bedecked with the year's collection for Arts and Crafts.

The program began with Grace singing "The Star Spangled Banner." James' skit, his adaptation of *Tom Sawyer*, was next. Aunt Polly with her broomstick, Tom painting the fence, Huck chewing on long grass, philosophizing–all produced a contagious roll of laughter but it was Vilma, behind an applied cover of black, who became the little boy from the South. As Jim, sitting cross-legged on the stage picking at her big toe, she drawled, "Tom, would ya like to see my hurt toe?" The audience had no idea of the line's significance but Vilma was a "show-stopper." She "brought down the house," as James was to tell me later on.

As Aunt Polly rushed to change into her costume for her role as Mrs. March, Alma recited the beautiful 23rd Psalm without a flaw, but without any intonation–it was one long flat monotone.

Next on the program was "Paul Revere's Ride" with Daniel and his boys. With all the difficulties of the past days, I had paid little attention to this group as I knew Daniel would not fail in his undertaking. What I had not expected was that Daniel, too, possessed a flair for presentation.

To my utter surprise the six boys, pyramided in size, marched onto the stage in black broad-brimmed Amish hats and red farmer's handkerchiefs at their throats. They leaned heavily on their rifles as they recited their adventures in the Concord countryside. No one in the audience appreciated them more than I–and all six eagerly scanned my face for approval–it was beaming.

Then came the ill-fated "Row, Row, Row Your Boat." Everything that had gone wrong in practice went doubled so on this night with the addition that John Henry took his new role very seriously and kept shouting, "Ahoy! Ahoy! Land!"

The last on the evening's program was the long awaited skit from Louisa Mae Alcott's *Little Women*–the deathbed scene of little Beth. A small cot was in the center of the stage. Clara Sue was dramatically laid out surrounded by her grieving Mother and sisters. All were weeping with loud sobbing effects and offering their noble and sombering soliloquies to the dying child when Clara Sue developed the most explosive type of hiccoughs. She tried to suppress them. Her face turned scarlet from holding her breath but this remedy only seemed to provoke the symptom and she emitted an even louder hiccough. The audience dissolved in hilarious laughter. No one could at first find a glass of water. When it did arrive, the scene was already in complete shambles. The only solution was to pull the curtains.

The audience left after a thoroughly enjoyable evening. Mrs. B. was to whisper to me on her way out, "I never laughed so hard in years." As I was saying good-night to the guests, little Sadie tugged at my sleeve, "I told you you'd have to have faith. Did you see, the daffodils did bloom?"

Yes, the daffodils did bloom–and March went out like a lamb!

APRIL

The beginning of this last month of school began in the middle of the week. It began like most others.

Clara Sue was having difficulty adding up her sums. Omar raised his hand to go to the toilet, to which I nodded my consent. Clara Sue was having a particularly trying time carrying the right hand figure and adding it onto the left hand column. Now Aaron also requested to go outside with an upraised hand. Without noting that Omar still had not returned he, too, was given nodded consent.

Within minutes, the two of them burst into the room shouting, "Fire! Fire!! Fire at the Bontrager's! Miss Todd, Hurry!"

Without a thought, I dashed for the front door and threw it open when I heard the entire room call out in unison, "April Fool!"

The children without a doubt had caught me completely unaware. So that this episode or similar ones should never become a repeated performance, I decided to read out loud the story of the "Little Boy Who Cried Wolf" after lunch.

"Miss Todd," said a chastened-faced Aaron, "There weren't no need to read us that. None of us would do anything so hurtful or mean if it weren't April Fool's Day."

Always my children are giving me lessons.

Later that same week Mrs. B. greeted me at her kitchen door with her "I have something to tell you" look on her face. I didn't need to ask.

"You don't need to worry anymore about turning little Vilma into an Amish."

Mrs. B. so loved to draw out a story. Suspense was her treasured ploy.

"What makes you say that?"

"My brother-in-law (the trustee) telephoned and said to tell you the township "Spell Down" has been cancelled–indefinitely."

Her tone and choice of words indicated there was much more to the story.

"Do you know why?"

"You know Samuel don't talk much–but I got my own ideas."

I only nodded knowing full well I would soon know all. Delivery rate, however, would be set by Mrs. B. To hurry would spoil the overall effect.

"In 1921 here in Indiana we experienced a terrible infantile paralysis outbreak. You must remember? Some call it poliomyelitis. Now such epidemics it seems happens more frequent in summer and early autumn."

This was going to be a long one. Mrs. B. was going way outfield.

"Lots of time the symptoms are headaches, colds and sore throats. All these complaints are also frequent in the springtime like now."

I nodded in agreement.

"Many mothers here in the country don't think it is a good idea to have get-togethers with the children from all different parts of the district."

I nodded, but had a questioning frown on my face.

"You're right. If this were true, then they wouldn't let them go to church–but, that's the Lord's house and He wouldn't let anything happen to them there."

Mrs. B. was wound tight and her tub-thumping seemed to have no end in sight.

"That's just the excuse my brother-in-law is giving out but the true reason is far different–or so I see it. As you have by now learned the church fathers and the Amish Bishops are powerful men. They even poke their noses into such things as a Spelling Bee. They feel that this type of contest is a form of competition when it goes outside the school proper which plants the seeds of pride and ambition into the blood of those who compete and even more in the one who wins. That, my lass, is the true reason the district "Spell Down" has been cancelled–they don't want their flock to ever forget 'humility.'"

— ♦ —

Walking to school during these early mornings in April makes me feel like an Indiana Evangeline in her "forest primeval." Everything is being born again and the freshness, the newness, can not but refresh one's own spirit.

Mrs. B. is having the hired man Wilbur spread manure on her garden. Like every other country woman this is her outside pride and joy. Eli and the other farmers are preparing the fields for corn planting. Winter is over and the work of spring is at hand. Mrs. B. was cutting up the potatoes for seeding while she upgraded my meager education on country life.

"Gotta get an 'eye' in each hill for it to see to grow. Potato plantin' is women's work. The men do seeding the oats while we be doin' this."

Never missing a knife stroke she continued my Indiana farm schooling.

"Corn planting usually takes place at the end of the month after the big rains are over–that's about the same time us women begin our spring house cleaning and white washing the fences around the farm buildings. I, particularly like the white–I do the posts of the grape arbor as well as the fruit trees around the house and orchard. Keeps the nasty insects away and it makes everything look right clean and proper."

"Spring Fever" was the collective disease in Froggy Bottom and there were a variety of remedies although no one really wanted to cure it. With the children, it manifest itself in a whimsical lethargy and with the women of the community with the cleaning-cleansing urge.

One morning Dorothy came in looking particularly pale and pinched. "My grandma sure is something–first she had to rub herself in oil of wintergreen 'cause her rheumatism is so bad and then she began on Grandpa and me. Time has come to thin the blood."

The girl looked me straight in the eye, "You'll get it too. Nobody is missed here."

What kind of barbaric treatment is given went through my thoughts. "How's it done?"

"Really it ain't so bad. Grandma boils the bark off the sassafras root to make a tea–it's orange colored and gives off a pleasant 'romatic smell. Grandma also adds some dried burdock seeds which she says is specific for boils and styes. Can't drink too much or it can give a nose bleed. Grandma and all the other women give it to their families 'cause they say after the winter, the blood is thick and has to be thinned."

As for the girls in my schoolroom, they were wearing woeful looks. They were anticipating the long sad months ahead when they would be parted from their dearest and most cherished friends. Their tragedy is contagious, but it is only a feminine malady.

Each and everyone brought their treasured leather-bound autograph books to school and they were passed from desk to desk. Each tried to outdramatize the other. On these beautiful sunny spring days, the girls are spending hours at their desks creating poetic adieus. After the message an appropriate border is drawn and painted in delicate water colors. These secret thoughts are communicated only to one's most intimate friends but, of course, each girl is expected to write in every other girl's book.

I happened to see Gladys' message to Grace. "To my dearest Grace." (In fact I thought there was a slight friction between the two.)

> *How will the months go by,*
> *Without my seeing your lovely smile on ruby lips?*
> *My heart will shatter and my lips will sigh,*
> *My only solace will be the remembrance of our*
>   *cherished friendship.*

In opposite corners with a framing border, Gladys had intertwined violets with musical notes. Coming from this rather tomboyish sixth grader, I am impressed by its creativity.

The boys expressed these heady days in much more physical ways. They stomped through the dank, musty woods always seeking and always finding treasure. Daily I would have a little reminder of their excursions on my desk. Perhaps it was a bunch of violets with just a trace of their distinctive woody fragrance or a jar filled with long stemmed fat, budding gray and fuzzy pussy willows. The boys, too, were romantic and I knew that I had many secret admirers.

Every morning I would hear the same question repeated among the boys, "Heard a whipperwill?"

And always there was some sort of negative reply, "Nope, not yet–saw a robin though."

One morning all the sixth and seventh grade boys were absent.

"Don't worry, Miss Todd–they'll be here," were Mary's comforting words. "They all arranged yesterday to get up at four o'clock. They had to do their chores first before they could get permission to go mushroom hunting. Chris and Abner knows best where to find them."

Around ten o'clock the boys burst into the schoolroom. All in very high spirits.

My pretended sternness was not even noticed as they plopped their finds on my desk. The boys were too excited to be bothered with the thought of any disciplinary action on my part.

"Miss Todd, you should see what we brought you," Bobby whipped open a sack and picked out several slender gray mushrooms, "Shaped like little thimbles these sponges are..."

If he had anything else to say it was going to have to wait as Charlie wanted his say, "Look at these–big soft spongy yellows–it was like goin' on a real treasure hunt this morning."

Chris said authoritatively and trying to maintain a very causal air, "True it was good pickin'–but just 'cause we knew where to look–side of fallen logs and old tree stumps."

"Miss Todd, you have Mrs. Bontrager jist fry these lovelies in sizzling butter and you won't never have tasted nothing so moorish," was Abner's contribution.

James who is usually the loquacious one was very silent. So much so that I finally asked, "Do you feel alright, James?"

"Oh yes, Miss Todd–it was just such a beautiful world that I am still under its spell. The light was soft and screened and so quiet and untouched. I could almost imagine that I would see that ethereal nymph Rima bounce out among the boughs."

To say the very least, I was absolutely flabbergasted. Mrs. Martin evidently had a much more complete classical library than I had ever thought. There are few adults whom I know who are acquainted with William Henry Hudson's "Green Mansions" and to hear it so matter of factly referred to in ordinary conversation by a sixth grader in a one-room schoolhouse in the Indiana countryside is rather amazing.

Indeed, the name April is well-chosen by the ancients for this month. Supposedly it is derived from the Latin word *aperire* meaning "to open." This could be an allusion not only to the budding and flowering of trees and shrubs but also to the mind.

The boys' exuberance was far from over.

Bobby burst out again, "We heard it! I swear we heard it."

Alma the ever vigilant watchdog of her religion sternly broke, "Robert Hartman, you know you have no right to use 'that word' in our presence."

"Oh, Almie, don't be such a hypocrite. Anyway, we did hear a whipperwill–loud and clear."

This last remark was enthusiastically corraborated by all the boys who had gone mushrooming. I did not understand its import until the following morning.

That afternoon I asked Dorothy why Alma apparently was so upset with Robert.

Dorothy looked at me rather quizzically before she answered, "I guess you're too old to remember well the ways of girls and boys. Almie's words didn't mean what they said. Of course, it's true the Amish aren't allowed to take an oath or swear by anything–but those were just an excuse–what she really was tryin' to do was call attention to herself 'cause she's got a secret-liking for Bobby."

Next morning every boy came to school barefoot and when I asked what this was all about, I was told.

"The whipperwill was heard."

Charlie embellished this statement with, "It's the law of the land–once we hear the whipperwill sing our ma's allow us all to go barefoot."

Of course that very day the whole troop of boys went wading in the Froggy Bottom pond on the other side of the road from the School. Pant legs were rolled up; all came down and all were wet.

They tried to soften my ire, for the boys were already well aware, that this latest action of theirs would result in being limited to the playground during school hours for the rest of the month.

"Miss Todd, you should have seen what we saw," chirped a very bright-eyed John Henry.

"What I do know is that you are all going to be in your beds with pneumonia. Imagine wading up to your knees in that cold pond water."

"She was so gentle and calm–only her eyes blinking," interjected Amos.

"James he explained it all to us," was Norman's comment.

"All right, what did James tell you?"

"This mother bird lines her nest by pulling out the downy feathers from her own breast," was the first remark from Orval.

"She's a mallard–she cleverly built her nest on a tiny island–she feels more protected like that says James." Omar wanted to go on, but Aaron interrupted.

"James says they usually lay from nine to eleven eggs–they are pale green in color–the female does most of the caring like our mothers."

The older boys were smiling broadly at my apparent discomfort. They knew that they had provided an interesting lesson in natural science for the younger ones which I would have to acknowledge.

"Miss Todd, did you know that a wild drake is monogamous?" asked James.

"What is monog..." stumbled Orval.

"It means he has only one wife," said James. Then he added, "Did you know that the domesticated male ducks are polygamous?"

"What does poly... mean?" again questioned Orval.

"It means that he has more than one wife," said James. "How would you explain and interpret this abnormality–if it is one, Miss Todd?"

I passed the remark off noncommittally. Is it possible that I saw a naughty glint in James' eye?

—◆—

The feeling that school will soon be over for the year is definitely in the air. Although there is a certain elation it is my impression that there is a great deal of wistfulness, too.

Four months is a very long time. Much can happen and change in our lives during such a time span.

When home for the weekend, I went to the Palm Sunday church service in Waterford. There I met a young man, Norris Long, from the county agricultural extension program. He is in charge of the volunteers who make up the local 4-H leadership.

Norris is one whom God never endowed with good looks. He has a long beaky nose set between two beady myopic eyes which are framed behind steel-rimmed spectacles. His ardent enthusiasm for life and his cause eclipse any physical lacks he may have. Never have I heard the 4-H program so explained and lauded. I was caught up with his fervor and asked if he would speak to the pupils at Froggy Bottom. Much to my delight, it was arranged for the following Friday afternoon.

Promptly at 2:30 p.m., Norris stumbled out of his sputtering car. The children were combed and glistening. A guest speaker of any category or subject is always a treat.

After his introduction, he opened with a few questions.

"Do I have any 4-H Club members present here today?" No.

"Have you heard of the 4-H Club?" Yes.

"Do you understand what it means to be a 4-H Club member?" No.

Norris was delighted. He had an unenlightened group that he could ply with information.

"The seeds of our 4-H clubs were planted around the turn of the century. It was and continues to be an agricultural project promoted by the U.S. government. It was created for rural school children like yourselves with the basic philosophy of 'learning by doing.' It is guided by a large group of volunteers–outstanding men and women of the community–farmers, homemakers, clergymen, teachers."

Bobby whispered to Charlie for everyone nearby to hear, "He may look like a scarecrow, but he talks like a reverend."

"Because there are so many and varying types of agriculture in our country, we currently have more than fifty different phases of homemaking and agricultural projects which can be undertaken."

The children were beginning to stir in their seats. The language used was stilted.

"Each community has a set of leaders and they are there to aid and guide the young person throughout his chosen project. The overall object of the Club is to develop constructive citizenship, leadership and the intelligent ability to cooperate..."

Bobby again whispered, this time to Omar, "Sounds like he knows the folder by heart."

Norris was wise enough to call a halt at this point. "I think it would be a better idea to have questions from the floor."

"What age can one be a member?" asked Gladys.

"Good question. From 10 to 21 years, both boys and girls can be members."

"What exactly do you mean by 'chosen' projects?" questioned Aaron.

"Each member of the 4-H Club pledges to carry out a definite project–this he has talked over with his leader–such as raising a calf or pig to maturity or some growing crop–for the girls maybe a canning experience."

"Does the Club have meetings?" came Omar's contribution.

"Of course, this is one of its 'growing' experiences–to be among other club members who are all undergoing similar improvement. As you are probably aware the 4-H Club emblem is the four-leaf clover with the letter H on each leaf signifying Head, Heart, Hands and Health. Our colors are white and green, white for purity and green for life and growth, the color of Nature."

"Isn't there a 4-H Club fair?" asked an unusually shy Grace.

"Yes. This is one of the big local events of the year. All the youngsters bring in their projects to be judged and compared with others in the same category. It's a time for fun and meeting other club members."

"I knew you'd want to know all about what the boys would be doing and where to meet them, Grace," was Mary's teasing jest.

"Of course there are also annual events. A member works his way up the ladder. There are delegates elected to the National Congress; there is a 4-H camp in Washington, D.C.... The possibilities that can result from this Club are innumerable, and above all, the member makes friends that last throughout his lifetime."

"Now that is all that I am going to leave you with today–here are a few informative folders that you should take and study with your parents. Mr. Bontrager, your Trustee, will be letting you know more about the local Club which is being developed. I will close my afternoon with you by repeating the 4-H pledge. I pledge:

> My Head to clearer thinking
> My Heart to greater loyalty
> My Hands to larger service and
> My Health to better living, for My Club,
> My Community and My Country."

After teaching nearly a whole school year I evidently still did not know my pupil's mentality. I thought there would be genuine interest in the 4-H. Norris Long had aroused no real concern nor any wish on their parts for active participation. Poor Norris came and went without even causing a ruffle or ripple.

That night I voiced my disappointment to Mrs. B. who along with her brother-in-law are involved in bringing the 4-H into the community. She wisely pointed out and said soothingly, "Child, Rome weren't built in a day. These children are integrated into their families–theirs is a united work force. There is no time for what the parents would think of as frivolity. It's the parents we gotta educate. Teach them times are changin.' They must see that their children's lives could be fuller, more productive."

"Once informed–Have you ever known any parent to deny his child something for his betterment? Patience–it's a great virtue."

—◆—

Since the boys' pond experience–and rare as it would seem not one of them caught a cold–they were allowed to play only on the school grounds. So restricted, James, always the inventive leader, decided they should build a kite. Bobby obtained fine and light wooden sticks and pin nails from his father. Light-weight cloth was next to be found. Gladys who was not supposed to be helping the boys was the one who came up with the acceptable idea of using old washed flour bags.

Design became the next problem. The artist in Abner wanted a triangular base with a semicircular head, "It would be beautiful like a bird."

James won out as usual, "Since we have never built a kite before, I think it should be as simple as possible–diamond-shaped."

Several days were taken up with this creation and I was only to hear snippets usually reported by my three third graders who are the most able of gossip mongers.

The current problem evidently is the tail. Again James was reported to have said, "It has to be long to give it balance."

Then came the subject of the string or cord, again James, "It has to be stiff but light. I understand the meteorologists..."

"What's a meteorologist?" asked Aaron. "James, I don't understand when you use such big words."

"Somebody who studies the weather by using kites."

Gladys who does not always like to be outshone by James added, "Remember the story of Benjamin Franklin who studied electricity with his kite."

Nor did James liked to be upstaged. "Gladys, you do have the capacity to oversimplify matters. Benjamin Franklin demonstrated with his kite that the kite attracted electricity from the air, thus proving the electrical nature of lightning."

"James, we still have not solved the stiffened string–how can we have it rigid and still light?"

"Have you boys ever thought of starching the string?" was Gladys' rather sardonic comment.

"Occasionally housewives come up with a good enough answer. Let's give it a try," was James' equally sarcastic reply.

Several more days went by and still the kite was not airborne.

"James, I don't see why you didn't have this idea in March when we had all those winds," was John Henry's observation.

I was leafing through the latest teacher's manual looking for Easter decoration suggestions when the three third graders burst in, "Don't you want to see the launch, Miss Todd?"

Without any hurried effort on my part I walked with the three and stood looking around, at first seeing nothing; then I gasped and shouted, "James! Stop it at once!"

There on top of the woodshed stood a small but very frightened Amos. How he had been placed on the roof, I still do not know.

Within minutes the little boy with a crumpled kite was again down on the ground. "I weren't really scair't of the height, Miss Todd, it were only the thought that maybe lightning might strike me."

I gave Amos an affectionate hug. "That you don't have to worry about–there is only lightning when there is thunder. James! The paddle–bring it to me!"

The paddling was insignificant. The worst punishment given to James was what he considered as being demeaningly abased before his classmates. He is thoroughly abashed.

—◆—

Easter time in my own home is associated with coloring eggs, rabbits, "Bunnies" real and otherwise, chocolate eggs, baby chicks, ham on Sunday, lilies in the church, something new to wear, preferably a hat, and an egg hunt. I was looking forward to bringing my Easter time to Froggy Bottom.

Never have the lower three grades ever questioned any of my decisions. They are now busy snipping out pink and blue paper bunnies for the curtains. The upper grades greeted my Easter festive activities with a certain skepticism, at best an indifferent tolerance.

My one big plan was to initiate an Easter Egg Hunt. I bought twenty-five eggs from Mrs. B. and then hard-boiled them.

The "function" was carefully described to the children as they had never heard of this event. As I told them–everyone was to color and decorate their egg, one to be given to each child. They were then to be placed into a big egg basket on my desk. During the night the Easter Bunny would take and hide them all. On Thursday afternoon the children would each be given a paper bag and sent out to find as many eggs as possible. When I would ring the handbell, they would have to return. The one who had found the most eggs would be given a prize. The child whose egg was chosen as the most beautifully decorated would be given another. I did not tell them that the Olympia Candy Kitchen in Goshen had donated a chocolate egg and rabbit to be used as prizes. My proposed Easter Egg Hunt was received with nary a smile or question.

"Hunting eggs must seem like fun to Miss Todd," I overheard Emma say to Sadie.

"Probably 'cause she don't do it everyday."

The children were clustered inside during morning recess–the skies had just opened up with a sudden spring shower. I decided to use the time with the help of Susie and Katie to water and clean up the potted plants. A huddle of boys never heard us edge near.

"Oh, come on, Bobby it'll be fun. What you goin' to do Friday afternoon anyway?"

Friday afternoon there would be no school as it was Good Friday. So far I found none of the children nor their parents planning to attend any church services on this day. As this is a conservatively religious community, I found it most strange that Easter played such a minor role in their lives. Easter is treated with almost a nonchalance. Another question mark?

"Charlie, Ma told me I was to gather dandelion heads—she needs at least three quarts of flowers to make her wine."

"You know it always rains on Good Friday."

"Rain or shine, Ma wants her dandelions."

Back at the desk, I motioned for Dorothy to come over. "What religion are the Hartmans?" Before she could answer I continued, "I thought most people here frowned on drinking alcoholic beverages."

"Some sort of Mennonite. There ain't none that openly allows drinkin.' Why?"

"Bobby has to collect dandelion flowers so his ma can make wine."

"Oh, that's it," Dorothy gave a shrug. "Our dandelion wine is sort of a spring tonic supposed to give a better appetite, cleanse and calm you. Lots of womenfolk use it on their families. Give them a tablespoonful before meals for as long as they need it."

"Do you know how it's made?"

"Real simple." Dorothy thoroughly enjoyed answering all my questions about their ways of life. "Three quarts of dandy flowers to two quarts water. Let them stand in a crock for three days. Strain, then add about two pounds of sugar, a sliced lemon and one heaping tablespoon of fresh yeast. This mixture then stands for another four days before bottling. It's a good tonic."

That same morning again I was snipping the dead leaves off the plants when I overheard the older girls chatting–they, too, were unaware of my presence.

"Sometimes you have to treat them like children says my ma."

"My ma says that city folk don't grow-up quick as we do here in the country. They can't help it."

"But how long does this childishness last?"

"Don't rightly know–we just have to sort of pamper her–it will pass."

"Anyway there's only a few days left of school."

Then, and only then, did I perceive that I had been the topic of their conversation. My face was burning as I returned to my desk.

—◆—

All of a sudden it is here–the last day of school. Everyone is in a holiday spirit. Careful picnic plans have been in the making for the past week and a half. The yellow table is top-heavy with culinary contributions–baked beans from Mrs. Bender; potato salad, Gladys' mother; macaroni salad, the Yoder's; a jar of red beets and peeled, hard-boiled eggs from the Hostetlers; cracklins from Amos and Orval's mother; a huge jug of lemonade brought in by Grace. Mrs. Martin bought packages of marshmallows as a special treat. My contribution, two wieners and buns for each pupil purchased at a very special price from Weaver's Meat Market in Foraker. There was something brought in to eat from every pupil's home.

"Enough food here for threshers," quipped Gladys.

The best the children had prepared for me. Rather than the school grounds, we were going off to Farmer Mishler's woods in the Troyer family's big spring wagon.

As Daniel pulled into the school yard, all shouted "Surprise, Surprise!" What happiness they all radiated. Soon the food was layered into bushel baskets and youngster upon youngster. We were off–singing and laughing.

After a bumpy stretch of gravel road, Daniel turned off into a shaded lane. The canopied sandy path was cool and awesome. The children momentarily fell silent and then began to speak only in whispers.

The designated spot was a lovely small meadow in the midst of the woods. Daniel and the boys had been there before and prepared the setting–the fire-pit surrounded by small stones was already made; a wagon's end gate had been placed atop sturdy boulders to serve as our food table. A stack of carefully sharpened forked sticks stood in readiness for wieners and marshmallows.

Everyone tumbled out. I was to be treated as the "Queen of the Day." The older girls took over the table and its preparation. Daniel and his crew took up their task of building the fire. Blankets were spread out on the ground.

It was idyllic. The tall poplars and the tulips, Indiana's state tree, all stood around the meadow's edge, the fully leafy heads of the latter just beginning to show budding signs of their glorious flowers. Jack-in-the pulpits sprung up here and there and everywhere were carpeted spots of violets in moss and bright yellow buttercups. The whole scene was laid out in one big bright patch of sun.

After lunch we all lolled about super-saturated with food and exuding well-being. I had decided to give out my awards which I had allowed Brother Ralph to buy (perhaps this had not been my wisest decision). He bought all Horatio Alger books at 25 cents a copy: three from the "Tattered Tom" series, one each from the "Ragged Dick" and "Luck and Pluck" collections. Three went for the spelling awards–

Vilma, James and Grace. Best Arts and Crafts–Mary and Abner.

The conversation was slow and easy and quite naturally came around to summer plans.

"In May those of us who ain't got too much work to do will be going to Bible school at Yellow Creek Church," said Mary. "Last two weeks."

"Vilma and I are going to visit Aunt Lucy on the other side of Nappanee–there I'm jist goin' sit by the tracks and watch the trains go by–countin' and wanderin' where they're headed fer," added little Norman.

"Ain't any blood relation–just a woman who tries to do something nice for them two," whispered Gladys in my ear.

"After Fourth of July, Ma and I are going to Rochester by train–there my eyes will be made straight," said a very proud John Henry.

"In August we got two weeks of camp meeting," said Anna Mae. "We ain't got a cottage where we can stay like Grace, so we have to go every day."

Susie broke in, "It's real nice–we have picnics under big trees–there's lots of tables and grounds for us 'kids'–sorry, children–to run around."

"Our ma's don't make us go inside the pavilion to listen–only if we want to–it's awful hot," added Clara Sue.

"The flies buzz and the old men go snoozing off but all the women there are listenin' to the preacher," colored in Susie.

Then it was time to go back–a tired, but smiling and still-singing group jolted and bounced along to Froggy Bottom School.

Everyone, although exhausted, quickly gave me a helping hand in closing-up. Bobby and Charlie carefully took down and folded the American flag as they had been taught to do. The three third graders washed the blackboard.

"Do we have to wash off Abner's beautiful picture and your big and little alphabet border, Miss Todd?"

I nodded. A certain sadness had began to overtake us all.

The two first graders with Gladys' guidance were given the honored role of cleaning the erasers for the first time.

I gave Susie and John Henry each a daffodil plant for their perfect attendance record–they thought I had forgotten. Sadie was given one for "having faith."

Orval brought in the tissue from the outside toilets. Grace and Mary took down and folded the curtains. Dorothy helped me clean out my desk. My personal belongings and books were carefully heaped into the now empty bushel baskets.

"I brought you a little something I made–Grandma taught me to tat," Dorothy handed me a linen square with fine tatting around the edge. "I probably won't ever see you again."

"What a lovely handkerchief. I'll think of you every time I use it."

Daniel came up and formally began, "It's been a great pleasure knowing you, Miss Todd."

I would have liked to have given him a hug, but I knew this would be frowned upon. Overt signs of personal affection are not shown among country people. So I simply shook his hand and smiled.

Everything has been tidied up–it is all done. One by one the children trooped by saying good-bye. I stood on the upper steps of Froggy Bottom School waving until the last figure was well down the road. No tears, no sadness, only smiles.

Turning back I found the school looking much the same as when I entered it eight long months ago. Froggy Bottom has been stripped of all the touches my children and I had added. Only a wobbly yellow table remains to attest that our existence has been real.

Physical buildings change little during such a relatively short span of time, but the same can not be said of those who people them. The young naive girl who entered the portals of Froggy Bottom in September of 1922, no longer exists.

Froggy Bottom is where I began my teaching days. It was from here that the door of experience was to be opened wide for me. It was from here I viewed the entire gamut of emotions in all shades and hues among my pupils.

How could I ever be able to forget–tubby Amos, cuddly Katie, mischievous Orval, brilliant James, forthright Gladys, questioning John Henry, proper Daniel, humble Vilma, talented Abner, loyal Dorothy–or any of my other pupils? Each has left a vivid image of themselves upon my memory. How could I not remember the other personalities who influenced my life during these months in the country–motherly Mrs. B.; just and stern Mrs. Martin; wise Grandma Mast; inquisitive Mrs. Bender? All have added so much to my own being.

One of Froggy Bottom's maxims is "Don't look back or you'll become like Lot's wife." So be it. Nevertheless, whatever the future has in store for me, those days will be deeply colored by my first unforgettable days of teaching in a one-room schoolhouse.